AAOS

EMERGENCY
CARE AND TRANSPORTATION
of the Sick and Injured

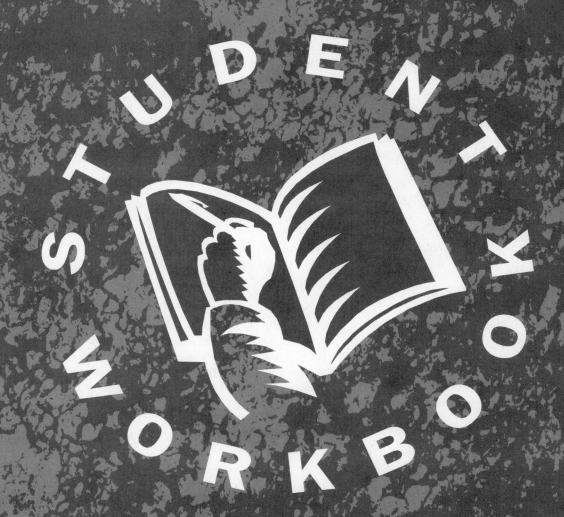

STUDENT WORKBOOK

CREDITS

Executive Vice-President: William W. Tipton, Jr., MD

Director, Division of Education: Mark W. Wieting

Director, Department of Publications: Marilyn L. Fox, PhD

Senior Editor: Lynne Roby Shindoll

Production Manager: Loraine Edwalds

Assistant Production Manager: Kathy M. Brouillette

Associate Editor: Gayle Ekblad

Production Editor: Rhoda Sterling

Editorial Assistant: Susan Baim

Editorial Assistant: Katy O'Brien

Secretary: Brigid Flanagan

Design: Pamela Hutton Erickson

Sixth Edition:

ISBN 0-89203-108-5

Published and distributed by: American Academy of Orthopaedic Surgeons

This *Student Workbook* is intended solely as a guide to the appropriate procedures to be employed when rendering emergency care to or transporting the sick and injured. It is not intended as a statement of the standards of care required in any particular situation, because circumstances and the patient's physical condition can vary widely from one emergency to another. Nor is it intended that this *Student Workbook* shall in any way advise emergency personnel concerning legal authority to perform the activities or procedures discussed. Such local determinations should be made only with the aid of legal counsel.

SIXTH EDITION

EMERGENCY CARE AND TRANSPORTATION OF THE SICK AND INJURED

STUDENT WORKBOOK

LYNN A. CROSBY, MD
DAVID G. LEWALLEN, MD

AMERICAN ACADEMY OF ORTHOPAEDIC SURGEONS

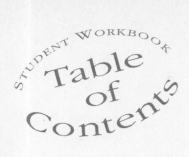

Student Workbook

Section 1
Preparing to Be an EMT-B

Section 2
Airway

Section 3
Patient Assessment

Section 8
Appendices

Answer Key

Introduction to Emergency Medical Care

For each of the terms in the left column, select the most appropriate description in the right column. Each description may be used once, more than once, or not at all.

1. _____ EMT-Basic

    A. an individual with extensive training in advanced life support and advanced assessment and treatment skills

2. _____ emergency medical services

    B. the first medically trained person to arrive at the scene of sudden illness or injury

3. _____ First Responder

    C. a physician who authorizes or delegates the privilege to perform medical care in the field

4. _____ EMT-Intermediate

    D. physician instructions given directly (on-line) or indirectly (off-line) to EMTs in the field

5. _____ medical director

    E. an individual trained in specific aspects of advanced life support, such as IV therapy

6. _____ medical control

    F. an individual trained for approximately 110 hours in emergency care techniques

7. _____ EMT-Paramedic

    G. the combined efforts of several professionals and agencies to provide prehospital emergency care to the sick and injured

Mark the following statements about the emergency medical services (EMS) system T for true or F for false.

8. _____ As an EMT-B, you must obtain assessment skills that will allow you to describe the patient's condition to the physician.

9. _____ The EMT-B is certified by the federal government to be competent.

10. _____ Under Title II of the Americans with Disabilities Act (ADA), an EMT-B is responsible for ensuring that disabled patients receive equal patient care.

11. _____ An EMT-B's first responsibility is for his or her safety and the safety of others at the scene.

12. _____ The medical director only authorizes on-line medical direction.

13. _____ According to the ADA, disabled patients must have equal access to information about their medical problems.

14. _____ The Department of Transportation is an EMS organization that promotes education, licensure, and certification of EMT-Bs.

15. _____ Quality improvement is a system of internal and external reviews and audits of all aspects of an EMS system.

Mark the following statements about emergency care training T for true or F for false.

16. _____ Basic First Aid and the First Responder training programs teach basic life-saving measures.

17. _____ Basic First Aid training should be taught only to adults as children are not capable of mastering this training.

18. _____ A First Responder should attempt to gain access to the patient and then call for additional help.

19. _____ First Responders should be trained in CPR.

20. _____ An EMT-B has completed training in advanced pharmacology and IV therapy.

21. _____ EMT-Bs will take over patient care from First Responders but may continue to use their help if needed.

22. _____ Volunteer EMTs have a lesser need for continuing education because they are not working full-time.

23. Which of the following statements about an EMT-B's professional appearance and conduct is **FALSE?**

A. Moral and ethical standards must be of the highest order.

B. Knowledge and skills must be updated and expanded through continuing education.

C. An EMT-B must recognize his or her personal limitations and accept constructive criticism.

D. Because death is an unfortunate, yet routine part of the job, counseling loved ones regarding death benefits may be necessary.

24. Which of the following methods is **NOT** considered on-line medical control?

A. Radio

B. Protocols

C. In person

D. Telephone

25. An EMT-B can provide medical care:

A. under an EMT-B license.

B. through the medical director's authority.

C. under the hospital's medical jurisdiction.

D. under the direction of the nurse on the ambulance.

26. Which of the following is **NOT** a principal responsibility of an EMT-B?

A. Traffic control

B. Patient assessment

C. Lifting and moving of patients

D. Record keeping and report writing

27. List six requirements that an EMT-B must meet to become certified.

28. Name three types of off-line medical control.

29. EMT-B training is divided into three main categories, with the most important category being the care of life-threatening conditions. List seven activities you must perform as you provide lifesaving care of a sick or injured patient.

30. The EMS system is made up of various components that work together to provide patients with the best emergency care in the shortest time possible. List six partners in the EMS system.

The Well-Being of the EMT-B

1. When a loved one or friend dies, feelings and emotions are part of the grieving process. Place, *in correct order from 1 to 5*, the stages of the grieving process.

    _____ depression

    _____ denial

    _____ acceptance

    _____ bargaining

    _____ anger

Mark the following statements about the emotional aspects of emergency care T for true or F for false.

2. _____ You will likely feel emotion regarding the death of a patient.

3. _____ During a stressful situation, you should tell the patient "everything will be all right."

4. _____ Feelings of guilt can cause a patient to have an unusual emotional response after an injury or illness.

5. _____ Patients should not be given the opportunity to express their fears and concerns because they will become even more upset.

6. _____ Children and the elderly may become terrified or feel rejected when separated from family members.

Mark the following statements about coping with stress and lifestyle changes T for true or F for false.

7. _____ To avoid burnout, you need to be in good physical and mental health.

8. _____ The proteins in meat, fish, chicken, beans, and cheese are immediately converted to fuel by the body.

9. _____ The stress that is part of an EMT-B's job requires a high energy output.

10. _____ Rotating your schedule or varying your call volume increases your stress level.

11. _____ A critical incident is an event that causes anxiety and mental stress to emergency workers.

12. _____ CISD meetings are investigations held immediately after a critical incident.

Mark the following statements about body substance isolation (BSI) techniques T for true or F for false.

13. _____ Handwashing is one of the most effective ways to control disease transmission.

14. _____ Vinyl gloves do not offer adequate protection.

15. _____ Double gloves should be worn if there is massive bleeding.

16. _____ Heavy-duty utility gloves should be worn for cleaning and disinfecting the unit.

17. _____ Goggles are the best protection against blood splatters into the eyes.

18. _____ A High-Efficiency Particulate Air (HEPA) respirator should be placed on a patient with a possible airborne disease.

Mark the following statements about hazards T for true or F for false.

19. _____ At a hazardous materials incident, you should not begin caring for patients until either they have been moved away from the scene or the scene is safe for you to enter.

20. _____ Power lines that are not sparking can be moved aside.

21. _____ Just before a lightning strike, you may feel a tingling sensation on your skin.

22. Which of the following statements about turnout gear is **FALSE?**

A. It provides head-to-toe protection.

B. It is lightweight and allows full range of motion.

C. It acts as a barrier to high external temperatures.

D. It uses different layers of fabric to keep water away from the body.

23. Which of the following steps at the scene should **NOT** be taken?

  A. Make sure there is enough lighting.

  B. Park the ambulance at a safe distance.

  C. Mark the scene with warning devices.

  D. Check a vehicle's stability by rocking or pushing on it.

24. When you are dealing with a dying patient, you should:

  A. distance yourself from the situation.

  B. treat him or her with respect and dignity.

  C. use a firm tone of voice and command the situation.

  D. reassure the patient and the family, even if there is no hope.

25. Following body substance isolation (BSI) techniques includes the use of:

  A. gloves, gowns, shoecovers, and eyeglasses.

  B. gloves, gowns, SCBAs, and thermal underwear.

  C. handwashing, gloves, gowns, and shoecovers.

  D. handwashing, gloves, eye protection, and masks.

26. One indicator of inadequate hydration is:

  A. frequent urination.

  B. infrequent urination.

  C. light yellow urine.

  D. excessive perspiration.

27. Which of the following food groups is the most reliable source of long-term energy production?

  A. Fats

  B. Proteins

  C. Simple sugars

  D. Complex carbohydrates

28. What is a Critical Incident Stress Debriefing (CISD) and what is its purpose?

29. A condition of chronic fatigue and frustration that results in increasing stress over time is called:

30. Define body substance isolation (BSI).

31. List five common hazards in a fire.

32. List eleven warning signs of stress.

33. List six immunizations that are recommended for the EMT-B.

Medicolegal and Ethical Issues

For each of the terms in the left column, select the appropriate definition in the right column. Each definition may be used once, more than once, or not at all.

1. _____ implied consent

2. _____ expressed consent

3. _____ abandonment

4. _____ battery

5. _____ assault

6. _____ advance directive

A. failure to continue treatment

B. written documentation that a competent patient uses to specify medical treatment should he or she become unable to make decisions

C. unlawfully placing a patient in fear of bodily harm

D. a patient expressly authorizes you to provide care or transport

E. touching a patient or providing emergency care without consent

F. a patient who needs immediate medical care to prevent death or permanent injury is given treatment under the legal assumption that he or she would want treatment

G. written documentation that gives medical personnel permission not to attempt resuscitation in the event of cardiac arrest

Mark the following statements about the legal aspects of emergency care T for true or F for false.

7. _____ Failure to provide care to a patient once you have been called to the scene is considered negligence.

8. _____ For expressed consent to be valid, the patient must be a minor.

9. _____ Expressed consent can be in the form of words or a nod of agreement.

10. _____ Do not resuscitate (DNR) orders give the EMT-B permission not to attempt resuscitation in the event of cardiac arrest.

11. _____ If a patient is unconscious and a true emergency situation exists, the doctrine of implied consent applies.

12. _____ Failure to perform important or necessary techniques is considered abandonment.

13. _____ In most states, EMT-Bs have the authority to pronounce a patient dead.

14. _____ If an EMT-B discloses patient treatment information without consent, he or she may be liable for a breach of confidentiality.

15. _____ In most states, patient records may be released when a legal subpoena is presented.

16. _____ Third-party payment billing forms may not be completed without written consent.

17. Which of the following medical report information is **NOT** considered confidential?

A. Patient history

B. Treatment given

C. Assessment findings

D. EMT-B's identification

18. In addition to legal responsibilities, you have certain ethical responsibilities to your patient. Which of the following is **NOT** considered an ethical responsibility?

A. Honest reporting

B. Obtaining expressed consent

C. Physical needs of the patient

D. Emotional needs of the patient

19. A conscious individual needing emergency medical care gives you a nod of agreement. This type of consent is called:

A. implied.

B. expressed.

C. informed.

D. applied.

20. Which of the following is **NOT** one of the four elements that must be present for the legal doctrine of negligence to be applicable?

   A. Duty

   B. Cause

   C. Abandonment

   D. Breach of duty

21. Which of the following statements regarding the guidelines for advance directives is **FALSE?**

   A. When in doubt, resuscitate.

   B. In a health care facility, a written physician's order is not required for DNR orders to be valid.

   C. The EMT-B should review state and local protocols and legislation regarding advance directives.

   D. Patients have the right to refuse treatment, including resuscitative efforts, if they can communicate their wishes.

22. An unconscious individual needing immediate emergency medical care to prevent permanent physical impairment or death would be considered to have given which type of consent?

   A. Implied

   B. Expressed

   C. Informed

   D. Applied

23. Which of the following acts is legally and ethically the most serious act an EMT-B can commit?

   A. Assault

   B. Battery

   C. Abandonment

   D. Obtaining only verbal consent

24. In many states, certain conditions allow a minor to be treated as an adult for the purpose of consenting to medical treatment. List three of these conditions.

25. When does your responsibility for patient care end?

26. There will be some instances when you will not be able to persuade the patient, guardian, conservator, or parent of a minor or mentally incompetent patient to proceed with treatment. List five steps you should take to protect all parties involved.

27. You have been called to the home of an elderly woman with a terminal illness. The patient is in need of immediate medical attention. The relatives in the room insist that you not give resuscitative treatment, but you are hesitant because they have no written document. What should you do?

28. One of the legal means for disclosing information is with an automatic release. Explain what an automatic release does.

29. List two rules of thumb that courts consider regarding records and reports.

30. List four steps to be taken when you are called to the scene involving a potential organ donor.

The Human Body

For each of the terms in the left column, select the appropriate definition in the right column. Each definition may be used once, more than once, or not at all.

1. _____ anterior

2. _____ midline

3. _____ medial

4. _____ inferior

5. _____ proximal

6. _____ distal

7. _____ anatomic position

8. _____ midaxillary

A. body parts that lie closer to the middle

B. farther from any point of reference

C. lower surface of an organ or other structure

D. standing, facing forward, palms facing forward

E. median line or plane of the body

F. situated in the front or forward part of the body

G. situated above or directly upward

H. vertical line from the middle of the armpit to the ankle

I. back or dorsal surface of the body

J. closer to any point of reference

For each of the bones listed in the left column, indicate whether it is an upper extremity bone (A), or a lower extremity bone (B).

9. _____ acetabulum

10. _____ patella

11. _____ clavicle

12. _____ fibula

13. _____ calcaneus

14. _____ ulna

15. _____ acromion

A. upper extremity bone

B. lower extremity bone

For each of the muscle characteristics in the left column, select the type of muscle on the right.

16. _____ attaches to the bones

17. _____ found in the walls of the gastrointestinal tract

18. _____ carries out the automatic muscular functions of the body

19. _____ forms the major muscle mass of the body

20. _____ under the control of the nervous system and the brain

21. _____ found only in the heart

22. _____ responds to heat and cold stimuli

23. _____ can tolerate blood supply interruption for only a very short period

24. _____ responsible for skeletal movement

25. _____ ability to contract on its own (automaticity)

A. voluntary

B. involuntary

C. cardiac

For each of the parts of the nervous system in the left column, select the phrase in the right column with which it is associated.

26. _____ spinal cord

27. _____ central nervous system

28. _____ sensory nerves

29. _____ motor nerves

30. _____ brain

31. _____ peripheral nervous system

A. extension of the brain

B. transmits motor impulses to the muscles

C. brain and spinal cord

D. carries impulses to and from muscles of the body

E. carries sensations of taste and touch

F. located within the cranium

Mark the following statements about respiration T for true or F for false.

32. _____ The diaphragm and intercostal muscles contract during inhalation.

33. _____ The ribs move down and in during inhalation.

34. _____ During exhalation, the diaphragm and intercostal muscles relax.

35. _____ During exhalation, the diaphragm moves downward.

36. _____ During capillary/cellular exchange, cells give up carbon dioxide to the capillaries.

37. _____ Normal respirations for an adult are 15 to 30 per minute.

Mark the following statements about the airway of an infant or child T for true or F for false.

38. _____ The mouth and nose are smaller and more easily obstructed than in an adult.

39. _____ The tongue takes up proportionally less space in the mouth than in an adult.

40. _____ The trachea is softer and more flexible in infants and children.

41. _____ Infants and children tend to depend less heavily on the diaphragm for breathing.

Mark the following statements about the pulse T for true or F for false.

42. _____ The pulse is a transmitted pressure wave felt in the arteries and produced by ventricular contraction.

43. _____ The pulse rate is most easily palpated at the pulmonary artery.

44. _____ The pulse rate of a child will normally be higher than that in an adult.

45. _____ A brachial pulse is considered a peripheral pulse.

46. The diaphragm is a specialized muscle because it:

  A. entirely controls breathing.

  B. has sole responsibility for diffusion.

  C. performs both voluntary and involuntary functions.

  D. ensures that air pressure inside the lungs is equal to that outside the lungs.

47. A measure of the force by which blood moves through the body is called:

  A. perfusion.

  B. pulse rate.

  C. blood pressure.

  D. myocardial contraction.

48. A joint is the place where:

  A. a tendon attaches to a bone.

  B. a tendon attaches to a ligament.

  C. two bones come into contact.

  D. two ligaments come into contact.

49. What two types of nerve fibers make up the peripheral nervous system?

  A. Sensory and motor

  B. Central and peripheral

  C. Motor and connecting

  D. Motor and peripheral

50. In addition to protection and temperature regulation, what other important function does the skin perform?

  A. It produces sweat.

  B. It produces hormones.

  C. It manufactures red blood cells.

  D. It transmits information to the brain.

51. List three functions of the skeletal system.

52. List five major sections of the spinal column, including the number of vertebrae in each section.

53. Name four factors to be considered when assessing adequate or inadequate breathing.

54. List the three steps that take place during alveolar/capillary exchange.

55. Name four components of blood. Next to each component, describe its function.

56. Define perfusion.

57. Define systolic blood pressure.

58. Define diastolic blood pressure.

59. Name two anatomic divisions of the nervous system.

60. Name two major parts of the central nervous system.

61. Name three layers of skin.

62. Name two functions of the endocrine system.

63. On the accompanying diagram, indicate the common terms used to identify the location of areas or features of the body surface.

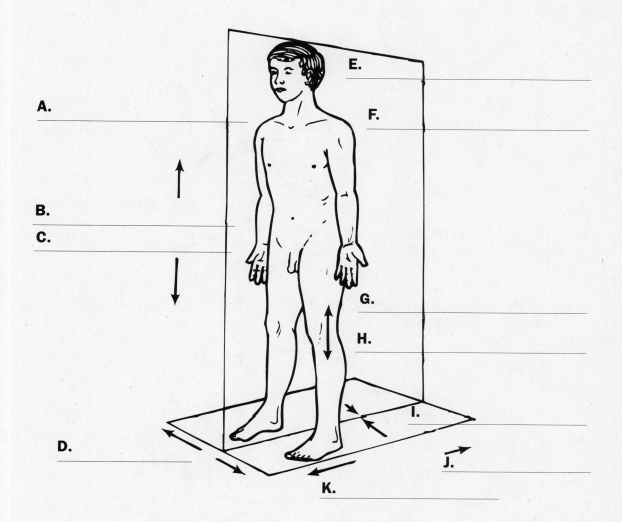

A. _____

B. _____

C. _____

D. _____

E. _____

F. _____

G. _____

H. _____

I. _____

J. _____

K. _____

64. On the accompanying diagram, label the major areas of the head.

A.

B.

C.

D.

E.

F.

G.

H.

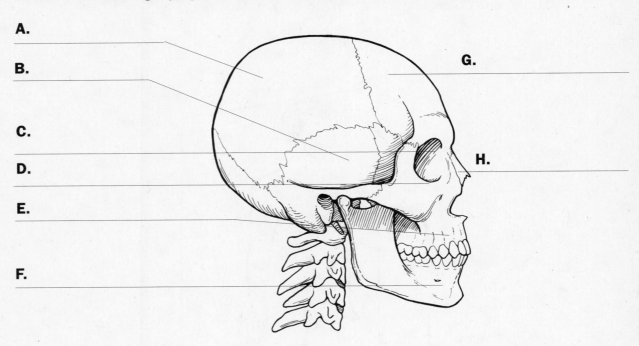

65. On the accompanying diagram, label the major landmarks of the head and neck.

A.

B.

C.

D.

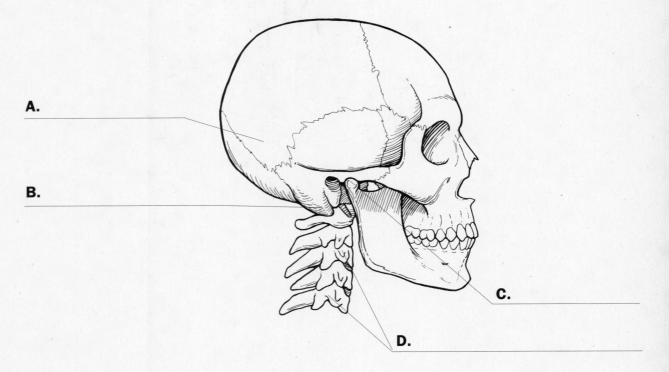

66. On the accompanying diagram, label the bones of the thoracic cavity.

A. _____

B. _____

C. _____

D. _____

E. _____

F. _____

G. _____

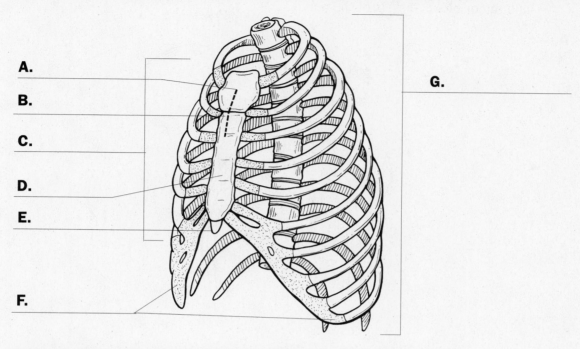

67. On the accompanying diagram, label the arterial pulse points.

A. _____

B. _____

C. _____

D. _____

E. _____

F. _____

G. _____

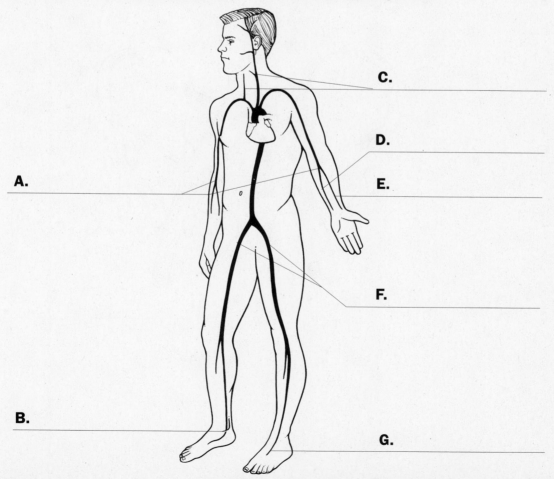

68. On the accompanying diagram, indicate the major bony landmarks, divisions, and major blood vessels of the pelvis.

A.

B.

C.

D.

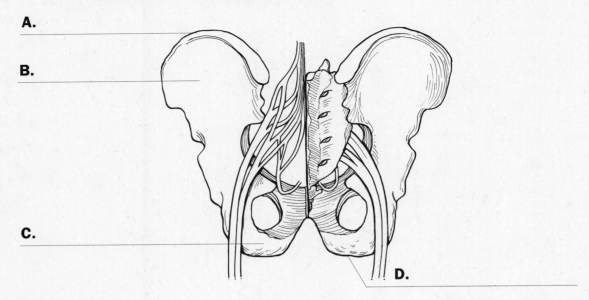

E.

F.

G.

H.

I.

J.

K.

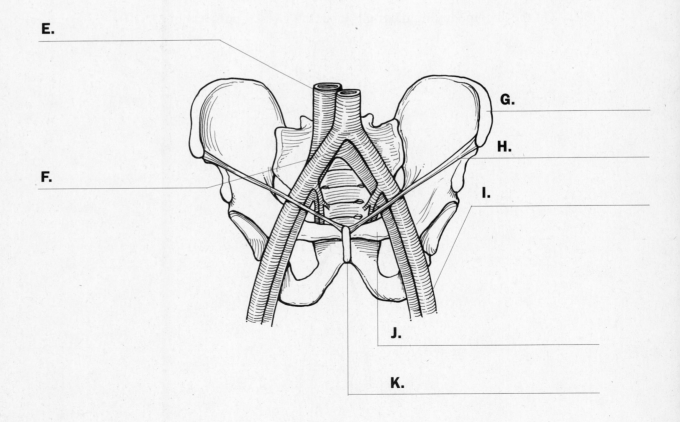

69. On the accompanying diagram, label the main parts and the bones of the lower extremity.

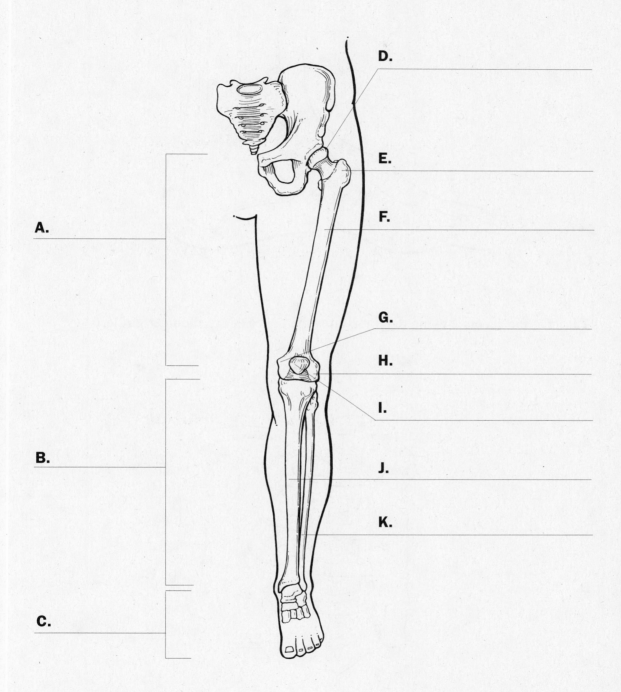

A.

B.

C.

D.

E.

F.

G.

H.

I.

J.

K.

70. On the accompanying diagram, label the parts of the ankle and foot.

A. _____

B. _____

C. _____

D. _____

E. _____

F. _____

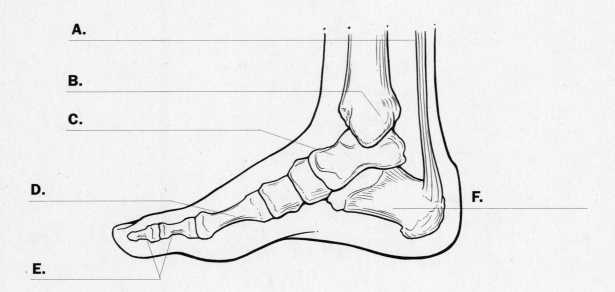

71. On the accompanying diagram, label the bones of the shoulder girdle.

A. _____

B. _____

C. _____

D. _____

E. _____

F. _____

G. _____

H. _____

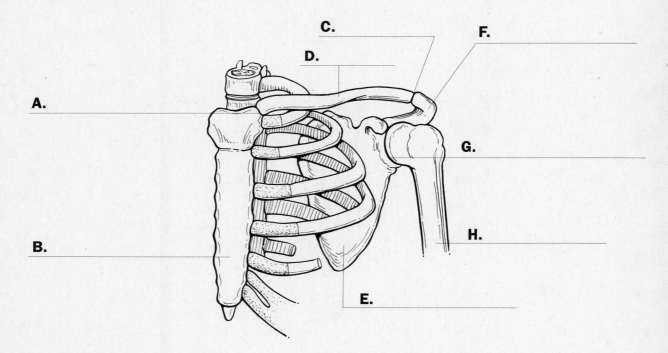

72. On the accompanying diagram of the posterior view of the elbow, label the major bony landmarks.

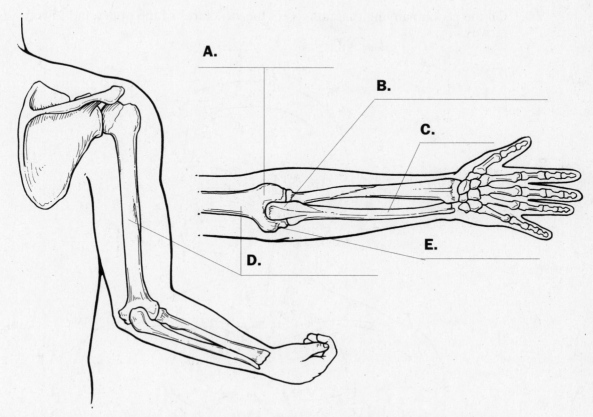

A.

B.

C.

D.

E.

73. On the accompanying diagram, label the bones of the wrist and the hand.

A. _____

B. _____

C. _____

D. _____

E. _____

F. _____

G. _____

H. _____

I. _____

J. _____

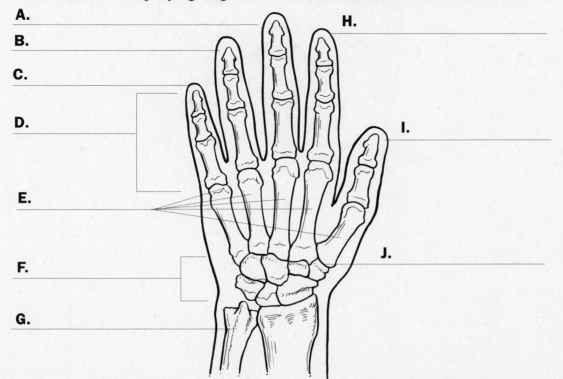

74. On the accompanying diagram, label the structures of the upper and lower airways.

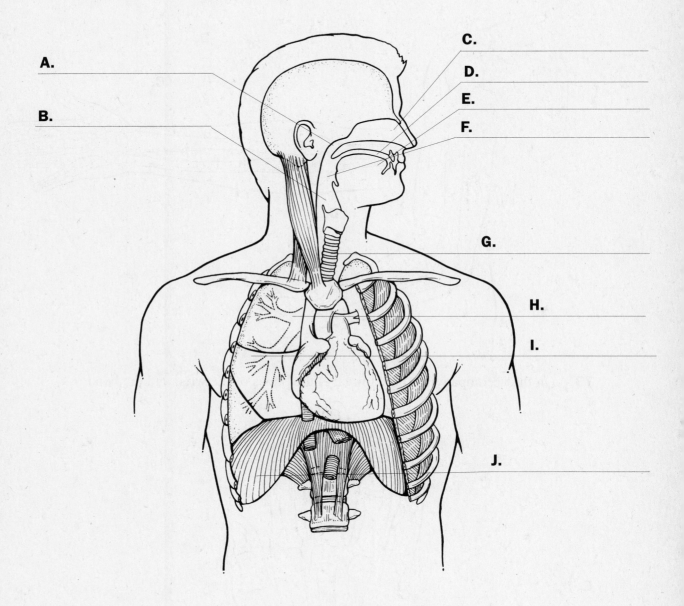

A.

B.

C.

D.

E.

F.

G.

H.

I.

J.

Vital Signs and Patient History

For each of the terms in the left column, select the most appropriate description in the right column. Each description may be used once, more than once, or not at all.

1. _____ pulse

2. _____ auscultation

3. _____ palpation

4. _____ perfusion

5. _____ blood pressure

6. _____ SAMPLE history

7. _____ sphygmomanometer

8. _____ capillary refill

9. _____ anisocoria

A. examination by touch

B. a blood pressure cuff

C. the pressure wave that is felt with the expansion and contraction of an artery

D. the pressure of the circulating blood against the walls of the arteries

E. listening to sounds within the organs, usually with a stethoscope

F. a condition where the pupil size is unequal due to a birth abnormality, eye drops, or a previous eye injury

G. the ability of the circulatory system to restore blood to the capillary blood vessels after it is squeezed out

H. a patient's history consisting of signs/symptoms, allergies, medications, pertinent past history, last oral intake, and events leading to the illness/injury

I. the process whereby blood enters an organ or tissue through its arteries and leaves through its veins, providing nutrients and oxygen and removing wastes

J. a condition displayed by the patient that you observe

Mark the following statements about baseline vital signs T for true or F for false.

10. _____ A pulse is an indicator of the condition of the heart.

11. _____ A blood pressure determined by palpation is less accurate than if determined by auscultation.

12. _____ Only the diastolic pressure can be measured by the palpation method.

13. _____ Increased breathing effort, grunting, and use of accessory muscles describes labored breathing.

14. _____ Rapid, shallow respirations are often associated with shock.

15. _____ The pulse is most commonly palpated at the femoral artery.

16. _____ The normal pulse range for a newborn is 140 to 160 beats per minute.

17. _____ To estimate systolic blood pressure in a male, you should add 100 to the patient's age.

18. _____ To assess skin color in an infant, you should look at the palms of the hands and soles of the feet.

19. _____ Cyanosis indicates a need for oxygen.

20. _____ BSI techniques should be followed when a patient is jaundiced.

21. _____ A rectal temperature is usually $1/2$ to 1 degree below an oral temperature.

22. _____ In death, the pupils are constricted and fail to respond to light.

23. Which of the following is largely responsible for regulation of the body temperature?

A. Skin

B. Muscles

C. Clothing

D. Ambient temperature

24. When you are assessing skin color, you should look at the:

A. tongue and eyes.

B. nail beds only.

C. nail beds and the back of the hands.

D. nail beds, oral mucosa, and the lining of the eyelids.

25. Normal diastolic blood pressure in adult males ranges between:

A. 40 and 90 mm Hg.

B. 60 and 80 mm Hg.

C. 65 and 90 mm Hg.

D. 90 and 140 mm Hg.

26. How many beats per minute is the average pulse rate in an adult?

A. 40 to 60

B. 60 to 100

C. 80 to 100

D. 100 to 120

27. Which of the following factors is **NOT** assessed when taking a pulse?

A. Rate

B. Volume

C. Reactivity

D. Regularity

28. Name five basic vital signs.

29. List four abnormal skin colors.

30. With most diseases and injuries, the systolic and diastolic pressures change in parallel fashion—in other words, both rise or both fall. Name three exceptions to this rule.

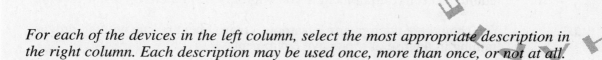

Lifting and Moving Patients

For each of the devices in the left column, select the most appropriate description in the right column. Each description may be used once, more than once, or not at all.

1. _____ short backboard   A. 6' to 7' long, rigid

2. _____ long backboard   B. immobilizes sitting patients

3. _____ flexible stretcher   C. carries sitting patients

4. _____ stair chair   D. separates into two or four pieces

5. _____ basket stretcher   E. used in water rescue

6. _____ scoop stretcher   F. 6' to 7' long, rolls up

Mark the following statements about lifting and moving T for true or F for false.

7. _____ The positioning, covering, and securing of an ill or injured patient for transportation is called "packaging."

8. _____ A portable stretcher is typically a lightweight folding device that does not have the undercarriage and wheels of a true ambulance stretcher.

9. _____ The term power lift refers to a posture that is safe and helpful for EMT-Bs when they are lifting.

10. _____ When lifting and moving ill or injured patients, the needs of the patient outweigh the risk of injury to the EMT-B.

11. _____ The use of adjunct devices and equipment such as stretchers, blankets, straps, and splints can make the job of lifting and moving a patient much more difficult.

Mark the following statements regarding good moving techniques T for true or F for false.

12. _____ Place the patient on a blanket, coat, or other item and drag the blanket, rather than directly pulling on the patient.

13. _____ If you can get behind the patient, put your hands under the patient's armpits, grasp the forearms, and drag the patient backward.

14. _____ One-person techniques for moving patients should only be used when immediate patient movement is necessary due to a life-threatening hazard and only one EMT-B is available.

15. _____ Entering a hazardous environment such as a smoke-filled area does not require protective equipment if you will only be in there for a few minutes.

16. _____ You should not attempt any hazardous environment rescue without proper training in the use of protective equipment.

17. _____ The Rapid Extrication technique is the preferred technique to use on all sitting patients with possible spinal injuries.

18. _____ Sitting immobilization procedures using vest-type or half-board immobilization devices can usually be accomplished within 2 minutes on untrapped patients.

19. _____ It is unprofessional for you to rehearse at the scene before moving a stable patient.

20. _____ When lifting a patient from a bed to a stretcher, the head of the stretcher should be placed at the foot end of the bed.

21. Which of the following factors is **NOT** a consideration when you are deciding how to move a patient?

A. Which hospital you are taking the patient to

B. Your physical and technical capabilities and limitations

C. The environmental risks and limitations that may endanger the patient, you, or your fellow EMT-Bs

D. The patient's problem, including the actual and possible threats to the patient's health and safety

22. Which of the following rules should be followed when lifting and moving patients and EMS equipment?

1. Only lift weights you can comfortably handle.

2. Use adjunct equipment whenever it is available.

3. Bend at the knees and hips and keep your back straight.

4. Establish a firm support base by placing both feet flat on the ground.

A. 1, 3

B. 1, 3, 4

C. 2, 3, 4

D. 1, 2, 3, 4

23. The most commonly used wheeled ambulance stretchers usually weigh approximately how many pounds unloaded?

A. 30

B. 50

C. 70

D. 90

24. When using the "power lift" position, it is important that you:

A. keep your feet close together.

B. keep your weight on your heels.

C. lift your upper body up before your hips rise.

D. relax your abdominal muscles to avoid cramping.

25. When two or more EMT-Bs are carrying a stretcher, they should:

A. lean in toward the load they are carrying.

B. lean away from the load they are carrying.

C. always face in the direction in which they are walking.

D. begin such a carry by first facing the stretcher and lifting with both hands.

26. When reaching overhead, you should avoid:

A. hypoextending your back.

B. hyperextending your back.

C. keeping your back straight.

D. reaching more than 7" in front of you.

27. You should avoid getting into a situation of having to provide strenuous support for more than how many minutes at a time?

A. 1

B. 3 to 5

C. 5

D. 15

28. Which of the following statements is true when you are moving a wheeled stretcher or chair?

A. It is better to lift it than to lower it.

B. It is better to push it than to pull it.

C. It is better to pull it than to push it.

D. It is better to revolve it than to rotate it.

29. Should you use bystanders to help lift and move a patient?

A. No, they should never be used to help.

B. Yes, if they are stronger than you.

C. Yes, but they must be shown what to do.

D. Yes, they should always be recruited to help.

30. The only time the patient should be moved prior to providing initial care, assessment, and stabilization is:

A. to get in out of the rain.

B. to avoid a traffic jam at rush hour.

C. when bystanders are available to help.

D. when the patient's life is in danger.

31. If, during an emergency, you must move a patient by pulling, you should:

A. roll the patient onto his or her side.

B. push the patient from either side.

C. pull along the long axis of the patient's body.

D. pull the patient sideways by the wrist and hip.

32. Describe how to position the following patients:

Condition	**Position**
A. Patient in shock	
B. Patient with chest pain or difficulty breathing	
C. Patient with suspected spinal injury	
D. Unresponsive patient without suspected spinal injury	

The Mechanics of Breathing

For each of the terms in the left column, select the appropriate definition in the right column. Each definition may be used once, more than once, or not at all.

1. _____ diffusion

2. _____ inhalation

3. _____ exhalation

4. _____ labored breathing

5. _____ agonal respirations

6. _____ airway

A. the passage above the larynx

B. nose breathing

C. the movement of air molecules from an area of high concentration to one of lower concentration

D. the muscles of respiration and the diaphragm are relaxed

E. the muscles of respiration contract

F. breathing during the third stage of labor of childbirth

G. gasping breaths after the heart has stopped

H. breathing with extra effort, either slower or faster than normal

Mark the following statements about the respiratory system T for true or F for false.

7. _____ As the diaphragm relaxes, inhalation occurs.

8. _____ One of the main functions of breathing is to allow oxygen to pass from the alveoli of the lungs into the blood.

9. _____ One of the main functions of breathing is to allow carbon dioxide to pass from the blood into the alveoli of the lungs.

10. _____ The upper airway includes the main bronchi, trachea, nose, mouth, and throat.

11. _____ The diaphragm is considered a voluntary muscle.

12. _____ The diaphragm is considered an involuntary muscle.

39

13. _____ During inhalation, the muscles in the chest wall and the diaphragm are active, causing the pressure to rise inside the chest cavity.

14. _____ During normal breathing, the accessory muscles of respiration contract to help squeeze air out of the chest cavity.

Mark the following statements about breathing problems T for true or F for false.

15. _____ See-saw respirations in infants is the normal resting pattern.

16. _____ Wheezing can only be heard with a stethoscope applied to the back of the patient.

17. _____ BLS is started only for cardiac arrest, not if there is a possible respiratory obstruction.

18. _____ In the field, respiratory arrest may appear the same as cardiac arrest.

19. Which of the following statements regarding problems maintaining an open airway in a child versus an adult is **FALSE?**

A. The trachea and larynx are softer.

B. The trachea and larynx are more easily compressed by external pressure.

C. Swelling of the epiglottis is more common.

D. The tongue is relatively smaller in children than in adults when compared to other structures.

20. What percent oxygen is contained in the air we breathe?

A. 11%

B. 16%

C. 21%

D. 78%

21. The brain stem normally controls breathing by increasing the respiration rate when the:

    A. nitrogen-oxygen levels fall.

    B. nitrogen level in the blood goes down.

    C. oxygen level in the blood goes up.

    D. carbon dioxide level in the blood goes up.

22. Which of the following is **NOT** a characteristic of normal breathing?

    A. Movement of the abdomen

    B. A regular pattern of inhalation and exhalation

    C. Retraction of the neck muscles during inhalation

    D. Audible breath sounds on both sides of the chest

23. A normal respiratory rate should be:

    A. 5 to 8 per minute in runners.

    B. 12 to 20 per minute in adults.

    C. about equal to the person's heart rate.

    D. more than 24 per minute in the elderly.

24. Which of the following is **NOT** a sign of abnormal breathing?

    A. Cyanotic skin

    B. Warm, dry skin

    C. Unequal breath sounds

    D. Muscle retractions between the ribs

25. If breathing stops, the lack of oxygen can cause:

    A. fainting due to brain damage.

    B. brain damage after 4 to 6 minutes.

    C. brain damage after 12 to 15 minutes.

    D. kidney damage before brain damage.

26. The control of respiration is normally determined by the:

A. size of the lungs.

B. person's physical condition.

C. oxygen level in the blood.

D. carbon dioxide level in the blood.

27. In children, nasal flaring is a sign of:

A. normal breathing.

B. labored breathing.

C. emotional distress.

D. an intact sense of smell.

28. If a person is not breathing, your first step should be to:

A. begin CPR.

B. perform a chest thump.

C. clear and open the airway.

D. give three quick breaths mouth-to-mouth.

29. When breathing problems occur in a conscious person, the heart rate usually:

A. goes up.

B. goes down.

C. stays the same.

D. is the same as the respiratory rate.

30. Which of the following defines alveoli?

A. Part of the vocal cords

B. Small air sacs in the lungs

C. A layer around the chest cavity

D. The most common form of pasta seen in cases of choking

31. On the accompanying diagram, label the structures within the lung.

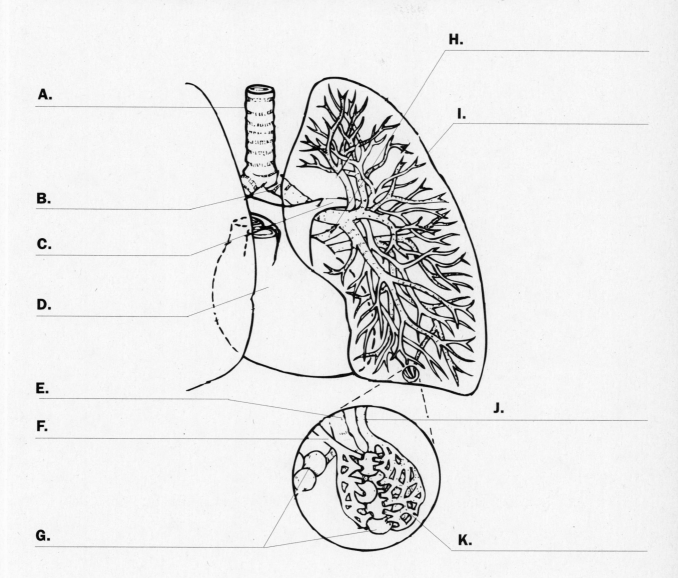

H. _____

A. _____

I. _____

B. _____

C. _____

D. _____

E. _____

F. _____

J. _____

G. _____

K. _____

Airway and Ventilation

For each of the terms in the left column, select the most appropriate description in the right column. Each description may be used once, more than once, or not at all.

1. _____ rigid suction catheter

2. _____ tonsil tip

3. _____ C-clamp

4. _____ barrier device

5. _____ oropharyngeal airway

A. a helpful, simple to use device for maintaining the airway

B. a method of maintaining the seal of a BVM device

C. best for suctioning the pharynx of adults

D. best for suctioning the pharynx of infants and children

E. has a one-way valve to prevent backflow of secretions and gases

F. requires advanced training for use

Mark the following statements about artificial ventilation T for true or F for false.

6. _____ You know that you are providing adequate ventilations if you see the patient's chest rise and fall.

7. _____ A flow-restricted, oxygen-powered ventilation device should not be used on infants and children.

8. _____ Mouth-to-mouth ventilations are best done with a one-way valve mask to prevent possible disease transmission.

9. _____ A bag-valve-mask (BVM) device with an oxygen reservoir can deliver more than 90% oxygen.

10. _____ A BVM device is easily used by one EMT-B.

11. _____ Barrier devices are designed to provide good infection control during mouth-to-mouth ventilations.

Mark the following mouth-to-mask ventilation techniques T for true or F for false.

12. _____ Use the head-tilt/chin-lift maneuver to open the airway.

13. _____ Pinch the nostrils between the thumb and index finger.

14. _____ Use a rapid, forceful breath to help open the airway and clear any obstruction.

15. _____ Feel for a pulse at the neck while exhaling into the patient's mouth.

Mark the following statements about the advantages of mouth-to-mask ventilation T for true or F for false.

16. _____ Both of the EMT-B's hands are free to help keep the airway open.

17. _____ Higher levels of carbon dioxide are in the exhaled air.

18. _____ A mask with an oxygen inlet works well for patients breathing on their own who need supplemental oxygen.

19. _____ The mask allows oxygen enrichment with inspired air.

20. The recovery position involves:

A. sitting bent over at the waist with the head down.

B. rolling the patient onto the right or left side with the hands placed under the cheek.

C. placing the unconscious patient faceup on a flat, firm surface.

D. placing the conscious patient faceup on a flat, firm surface with the head turned to the side.

21. The most common cause of airway obstruction in adults is:

A. food.

B. vomit.

C. dentures.

D. the airway's own tissues.

22. Which of the following is **NOT** a possible cause of airway obstruction?

A. Mucus

B. Vomit

C. Blood clots

D. Swallowing the tongue

23. Suctioning of the mouth and throat should be done:

A. whenever gurgling noises are heard.

B. whenever CPR is given for more than 5 minutes.

C. only if solid material such as food is present.

D. only if liquid material such as vomit is present.

24. During suctioning of the airway, it is important to:

A. insert the suction tip only to the base of the tongue.

B. use a rigid catheter when suctioning the nose.

C. suction as far down into the pharynx as possible.

D. suction for at least 30 seconds to ensure that all foreign objects are removed.

25. What percent oxygen is delivered by mouth-to-mouth ventilation using a barrier device?

A.   5%

B.   16%

C.   26%

D. 100%

26. Ventilation with a BVM device during external chest compressions should be delivered at a rate of:

A. once after every other compression.

B. once after every fifth compression, or twice after every fifteenth compression.

C. twice after every fifth compression.

D. three times after every tenth compression.

27. The total amount of gas in the reservoir bag of an adult BVM device is usually:

A. 10 to 15 mL.

B. 150 to 240 mL.

C. 500 to 700 mL.

D. 1,200 to 1,600 mL.

28. List four methods for opening the airway.

29. List five steps to properly position a patient without spinal injury for airway management.

30. Describe the three-part approach—look, listen, and feel—used to assess whether breathing has returned.

Airway Adjuncts and Oxygen Equipment

For each of the terms in the left column, select the appropriate description in the right column. Each description may be used once, more than once, or not at all.

1. _____ hypoxia

    A. airway adjunct inserted into the mouth to keep the tongue from blocking the upper airway

2. _____ nasopharyngeal airway

    B. a safety system for large oxygen cylinders to prevent the accidental attachment of a regulator to a wrong cylinder

3. _____ oropharyngeal airway

    C. airway adjunct inserted into the nostril of a conscious patient who is not able to maintain a natural airway

4. _____ American Standard System

    D. tube-like prongs to deliver oxygen into the nostrils

5. _____ nasal cannula

    E. dangerous condition in which the body's tissues and cells do not have enough oxygen after a period of time

Mark the following statements about airway adjuncts T for true or F for false.

6. _____ The nasopharyngeal airway is usually well tolerated and is not as likely as the oropharyngeal airway to cause vomiting.

7. _____ Patients with a gag reflex usually do not tolerate an oropharyngeal airway.

8. _____ To select the proper size oropharyngeal airway, measure from the earlobe to the corner of the mouth on the side of the face.

9. _____ You should consult medical control before inserting a nasopharyngeal airway in a patient with severe trauma to the head.

10. _____ An oropharyngeal airway does not allow you to suction the airway.

11. _____ Without an oropharyngeal airway, a patient may swallow his or her tongue.

12. To select the proper size nasopharyngeal airway, measure from the:

   A. tip of the nose to the chin.

   B. tip of the nose to the earlobe.

   C. earlobe to the corner of the mouth.

   D. corner of the mouth to the outer corner of the eye.

13. An oxygen cylinder should be refilled or replaced when pressure on the regulator reads less than:

   A. 10 psi.

   B. 500 psi.

   C. 2,100 psi.

   D. 10,000 psi.

14. The most efficient means of maintaining the airway of an unconscious patient believed to have a spinal injury would be to:

   A. insert a nasopharyngeal airway.

   B. insert an oropharyngeal airway.

   C. ensure that the head is tilted back.

   D. place the patient in the "sniffing" position.

15. Which of the following hazards of supplemental oxygen therapy in the field is **FALSE**?

   A. Oxygen itself can burn and explode.

   B. A spark or a glowing cigarette can burst into flames.

   C. A regulator removed from the valve stem while there is a pressure reading on the regulator gauge can cause injuries.

   D. Cracks, punctures, or a loose regulator can cause the cylinder to become a deadly missile.

16. In a cardiac arrest situation, you should always give the patient:

    A. low concentrations of oxygen.

    B. high concentrations of oxygen.

    C. oxygen cautiously, and only under direct medical control instruction.

    D. oxygen using a nasal cannula with the flowmeter set at 3 L per minute.

17. What is the significance of the star stamped next to the date on an oxygen bottle?

    A. It positively verifies that the bottle contains medical oxygen.

    B. It indicates that the bottle is certified as safe for 1 year.

    C. It indicates that the bottle is certified as safe for 10 years.

    D. It indicates that the bottle should be retested within 5 years of the stamped date.

18. The preferred method of giving oxygen in the prehospital setting is with:

    A. a nasal cannula.

    B. a simple face mask.

    C. a nonrebreathing mask.

    D. an oropharyngeal airway.

19. Pressure regulators reduce the pressure of gas in an oxygen cylinder to a workable level. List two final attachments that can be used to deliver the gas to the patient.

20. List two types of patients who should always receive supplemental oxygen.

21. List two types of flowmeters commonly used.

22. List two sizes of oxygen cylinders that are used most often and state where they are used.

23. Describe four steps to insert an oropharyngeal airway in an adult.

24. Describe the pin-indexing system and what it prevents.

Advanced Airway Management

For each of the terms in the left column, select the most appropriate description in the right column. Each description may be used once, more than once, or not at all.

1. _____ curved blade

   A. a plastic-coated wire that adds rigidity and shape to the endotracheal tube

2. _____ straight blade

   B. when placed on the laryngoscope and used for intubation, the tip goes just in front of the epiglottis

3. _____ stylet

   C. when placed on the laryngoscope and used for intubation, the tip is inserted past the epiglottis

4. _____ epiglottis

   D. an instrument that provides a direct view of the vocal cords

5. _____ intubation

   E. a thin valve that allows air to pass into the trachea but prevents food and liquid from entering

6. _____ laryngoscope

   F. the placement of a tube into the lower airway to protect and improve ventilation

7. _____ vallecula

   G. the voice box containing the vocal cords

8. _____ larynx

   H. the space between the base of the tongue and the epiglottis

Mark the following statements about endotracheal intubation T for true or F for false.

9. _____ The light in the laryngoscope will not work unless the blade is attached correctly.

10. _____ Endotracheal intubation is usually most appropriate for unconscious patients.

11. _____ There are three different sizes of ETTs.

12. _____ The balloon cuff around the end of an ETT holds 25 mL of air.

13. _____ Uncuffed tubes are used in children younger than 8 years old.

14. _____ When a wire stylet is used, it should stick out $1/2$" beyond the tip of the ETT.

15. _____ The three structures that need to be in a straight line for a proper intubation are the trachea, pharynx, and esophagus.

16. _____ Some medications may be given via the ETT.

17. _____ An end tidal carbon dioxide detector signals, by color change, that an ETT is in the proper place.

Mark the following statements about anatomy and the Sellick maneuver T for true or F for false.

18. _____ The Adam's apple is also called the thyroid cartilage.

19. _____ The cricoid cartilage is located above the Adam's apple.

20. _____ In some cases, an emergency airway can be inserted in the cricothyroid membrane.

21. _____ Pressure on the cricoid cartilage should be maintained after the patient is intubated or begins coughing and gagging.

22. _____ Three EMT-Bs are needed to perform CPR and apply the Sellick maneuver.

Mark the following statements about gastric distention T for true or F for false.

23. _____ Gastric distention does not interfere with artificial ventilation.

24. _____ Gastric distention can be minimized by using slow, 1- to $1^1/2$-second breaths.

25. _____ An orogastric tube can cause nasal trauma with bleeding.

26. _____ A gastric tube is used to decompress the stomach of a patient with gastric distention.

27. The Sellick maneuver is performed to improve visualization of the:

   A. trachea.

   B. pharynx.

   C. esophagus.

   D. vocal cords.

28. The blade of the laryngoscope should first be placed in the:

   A. left side of the mouth, then moved to the center.

   B. right side of the mouth, then moved to the center.

   C. center of the mouth, then moved to the back.

   D. back of the mouth, then moved to the base of the tongue.

29. The purpose of a balloon cuff on an endotracheal tube is to:

   A. hold the tube in the trachea.

   B. keep the tracheal rings open.

   C. prevent air from entering the stomach.

   D. prevent the contents of the stomach from entering the lungs.

30. The head and neck of a nontrauma patient who is to undergo endotracheal intubation should be placed in:

   A. flexion.

   B. extension.

   C. hyperextension.

   D. a neutral position.

31. To intubate properly, you must visualize the:

   A. larynx.

   B. trachea.

   C. esophagus.

   D. vocal cords.

32. Once an ETT is secured in place, you must carefully assess the patient's:

    A. position.

    B. gag reflex.

    C. vital signs.

    D. vocal cords.

33. Name three advantages of intubation in the unconscious patient.

34. List four principal purposes of a nasogastric or orogastric tube.

35. List six possible complications of endotracheal intubation.

Scene Size-up and Initial Assessment

For each of the terms in the left column, select the most appropriate description in the right column. Each description may be used once, more than once, or not at all.

1. _____ AVPU scale

    A. patients needing immediate care and transport

2. _____ body substance isolation (BSI) techniques

    B. a protective item that limits exposure to a patient's body fluids

3. _____ priority patients

    C. an overall initial impression formed to determine the priority for patient care

4. _____ barrier device

    D. a way of assessing the airway of an unconscious patient

5. _____ scene size-up

    E. the best way to reduce the risk of exposure to a communicable disease

6. _____ general impression

    F. a quick assessment of the scene and the surroundings

    G. a method of assessing a patient's level of consciousness

Mark the following statements about steps at the scene T for true or F for false.

7. _____ Scene safety is limited to ensuring that the patient is safe.

8. _____ Bystanders may interfere with patient care.

9. _____ Mechanism of injury refers to the type of injury received by the patient.

10. _____ In a multiple-patient situation, you should always call for additional help before caring for patients.

11. _____ You should use the head-tilt/chin-lift maneuver for an unresponsive patient with no spinal injury.

12. _____ A patient that can correctly tell you the date, the location, and his or her own name is said to be "alert and oriented times three."

13. _____ The chief complaint refers to what you think is bothering the patient the most.

14. _____ A responsive patient with respirations of greater than 12/min should receive assisted ventilations with a BVM device.

15. _____ The recovery position allows excretions to spontaneously drain from a patient's mouth.

16. _____ The bag-valve-mask device provides the easiest and most efficient delivery of oxygen.

17. _____ Body substance isolation (BSI) techniques require the EMT-B to wear protection only when the risk of contamination is high.

18. Which of the following statements about the pulse is **FALSE?**

A. The pulse is measured by palpating a vein at a pulse point.

B. A pulse point is an area where an artery lies close to the surface of the skin.

C. The pulse should be monitored continuously in most patient situations.

D. The pulse rate gives you a rough idea of the strength of the heart's contractions.

19. Assessing a patient's airway begins by:

A. opening the airway.

B. giving two full breaths.

C. watching the patient for air movement.

D. evaluating the patient's level of consciousness.

20. Which of the following defines triage?

A. The recording of each patient's chief complaint

B. The tagging of patients with numbers to establish a proper count of the injured

C. The sorting of patients by their injuries into smaller groups so that similar injuries are grouped together

D. The process of establishing treatment and transportation priorities according to severity of injury and medical need

21. Which of the following is **NOT** one of the steps for the jaw-thrust maneuver?

A. Place the fingers of both your hands behind the angles of the lower jaw.

B. Forcefully move the jaw forward.

C. Tilt the head back extending the patient's cervical spine.

D. Pull the lower lip down using your thumb so that the patient can breathe through both the nose and mouth.

22. You suspect a patient is faking unconsciousness. Which of the following methods should you use to determine if the patient is faking?

A. Pinch the patient.

B. Roll the patient over.

C. Drop an object on the patient.

D. Allow the patient's hand to drop on his or her face.

23. Which of the following statements about the initial assessment is true?

A. It is a comprehensive physical examination.

B. It provides a limited amount of information.

C. It does not include information about age, sex, or race.

D. It requires the EMT-B to use all his or her senses at all times.

24. Which of the following terms can be used to describe a patient's level of consciousness?

1. Alert

2. Responsive to verbal stimulus

3. Responsive to pain

4. Unresponsive

A. 1, 4

B. 2, 3

C. 2, 3, 4

D. 1, 2, 3, 4

25. Oxygen should be given to:

A. elderly patients with no history of emphysema.

B. trauma patients regardless of vital signs.

C. all patients with breathing difficulties.

D. only those patients who do not have emphysema.

26. The recovery position is used to help maintain:

A. cervical stabilization.

B. the trunk and spine in position.

C. a clear airway in an unconscious patient who has not had traumatic injuries and is breathing on his or her own.

D. a clear airway in a patient who has not had traumatic injuries and is not breathing on his or her own.

27. As soon as a patient's airway is cleared and breathing is stabilized, the next step in the initial assessment is to:

28. On occasion, you will not be able to safely enter a scene because of the need for extrication, hazardous conditions, or there are more patients than you can handle. What five questions do you need to ask yourself as you evaluate the need for additional resources?

29. List five basic steps of the head-tilt/chin-lift maneuver.

30. List six methods of controlling external bleeding.

31. You are assessing a patient's breathing. What three questions do you need to ask yourself?

Patient Assessment

For each of the terms in the left column, select the appropriate definition in the right column. Each definition may be used once, more than once, or not at all.

1. _____ mechanism of injury

2. _____ paradoxical motion

3. _____ crepitus

4. _____ symptom

5. _____ chief complaint

6. _____ distention

7. _____ sign

A. the act or state of being swollen

B. the way in which traumatic injuries occur

C. an objective physical finding

D. chest movement that is in the opposite direction of the normal rise and fall of breathing

E. something the patient experiences and tells the EMT-B

F. a crackling sound heard when two ends of a broken bone rub together

G. the patient's response to a general question such as "What's wrong?"

Mark the following statements about the steps of patient assessment T for true or F for false.

8. _____ The first steps in caring for any patient are the initial and rapid assessments.

9. _____ Priority should always be given to the ABCD.

10. _____ The "E" in the ABCDE of patient assessment stands for the EVENTS at the time of injury.

11. _____ A detailed physical exam must always be performed prior to transport.

12. _____ The "Golden Hour" refers to the importance of rapidly getting the trauma patient to the hospital within 60 minutes from the time of injury.

13. _____ You should stay at the scene until the trauma patient is stable.

14._____ You should record a few of the patient's own words when writing down the patient's chief complaint.

15._____ OPQRST helps you remember the bones of the hand.

16._____ The rapid trauma assessment and the rapid assessment of a medical patient are done for the same reasons.

17._____ A patient should be log rolled onto a backboard before the back is examined.

18._____ It is not necessary to always wear gloves when dealing with medical patients.

19._____ You should assume a spinal injury with any trauma patient who is under the influence of drugs or alcohol.

20. When caring for a trauma patient, you should:

A. treat shock as your first priority.

B. delay transport if the patient is unstable.

C. withhold oxygen if the patient is unstable.

D. maintain in-line immobilization of the cervical spine.

21. When lap seat belts are worn properly, they should:

A. never cause bruises.

B. lie below the iliac crests.

C. belt across the abdomen.

D. fit loosely over the hip joints.

22. If you suspect a spinal injury, the patient's spine must be immobilized in line at all times during your assessment of the back. This is best done by:

A. log rolling the patient.

B. placing the patient in the recovery position.

C. checking first for bony crepitance.

D. asking the patient where the pain is.

23. You should reassess an unstable patient's vital signs every:

A.   5 minutes.

B. 10 minutes.

C. 15 minutes.

D. 20 minutes.

24. You should reassess a stable patient's vital signs every:

A. 10 minutes.

B. 15 minutes.

C. 20 minutes.

D. 25 minutes.

25. Discoloration around the eyes (Raccoon eyes) or behind the ears (Battle's sign) may be seen when the patient has had a:

A. stroke.

B. head injury.

C. chest injury.

D. cervical spine injury.

26. Which of the following signs is **NOT** usually noted in your assessment of a patient's extremities?

A. Absence of pulse

B. Paradoxical motion

C. Loss of sensation

D. Loss of motor function

27. In what six areas can you question a patient to obtain a history of present illness using the acronym SAMPLE?

28. What do the initials in the OPQRST method of evaluating pain represent?

29. What is the purpose of the detailed physical exam?

30. List eight signs of injury you are looking and feeling for when conducting a detailed physical exam.

31. List 10 significant mechanisms of injury for adults.

Communications and Documentation

For each of the terms in the left column, select the appropriate description in the right column. Each description may be used once, more than once, or not at all.

1. _____ base station

2. _____ mobile radio

3. _____ hand-held portable radio

4. _____ repeater

5. _____ telemetry

6. _____ radio frequencies between 300 and 3,000 MHz

7. _____ radio frequencies between 30 and 300 MHz

A. a process in which electronic signals are converted into coded, audible signals

B. can go wherever the EMT-B goes

C. radio hardware containing a transmitter and receiver that is located in a fixed location

D. special base station radio that receives messages and signals on one frequency and then automatically retransmits them on a second frequency

E. UHF range

F. VHF range

G. VHF and UHF channels exclusively for EMS use

H. vehicle-mounted

In your radio report to the hospital, certain information is routinely included. Using the list below, indicate whether the information should be included in your report (A), or not be included (B).

8. _____ EMT-B's identification

9. _____ hospital destination

10. _____ estimated time of arrival

11. _____ patient's age

12. _____ patient's sex

13. _____ patient's name

A. Include

B. Do not include

14. _____ chief complaint

15. _____ history of present illness or injury

16. _____ patient's address

17. _____ patient's social security number

18. _____ patient's medications

19. _____ patient's date of birth

Mark the following statements about communications equipment T for true or F for false.

20. _____ A radio is actually at least two units, a transmitter and a receiver.

21. _____ Base stations typically have more power and much higher and more efficient antenna systems than mobile or portable radios.

22. _____ A cellular telephone is just another kind of two-way radio that is available for EMS use.

23. _____ The transmission range of a mobile radio is more limited than that of a portable radio.

24. _____ A dedicated line is a special telephone line used for specific point-to-point communications.

25. Which of the following reports is **NOT** usually transmitted by an EMT-B using the EMS communications system?

A. Ambulance status

B. Condition of the patient

C. Conditions at the emergency site

D. Diagnosis of the patient's problem

26. What federal agency regulates the use of communications equipment?

A. FTD

B. FBI

C. FCC

D. FDA

27. The alert and dispatch phase of an EMS call requires several important actions by the dispatcher. Which of the following actions should **NOT** be included?

A. Screen and assign priority to each call.

B. Dispatch and direct the units to the correct location.

C. Select and alert the appropriate EMS response units.

D. Provide information to the news media as to the patient's identity and extent of injuries.

28. Which of the following devices does the dispatcher use to alert an EMS crew to an emergency call?

      1.   Pager

      2.   Desktop monitor radio

      3.   Dedicated hot line

      4.   Direct radio communication

A. 2, 4

B. 3, 4

C. 1, 3, 4

D. 1, 2, 3, 4

29. You have just received an alert from the dispatcher. You should first:

A. go to the location.

B. alert medical control.

C. check the gas and oil and then respond.

D. acknowledge the information received.

30. Your EMS crew has encountered some problems while responding to an emergency scene. Who should you advise of the situation?

A. Medical control

B. The police

C. The dispatcher

D. The fire department

31. When you reach the scene, your arrival report to the dispatcher should include:

A. the patient's name.

B. your name.

C. any obvious details you see during size-up.

D. the ID of any other emergency units on the scene.

32. Which of the following statements about a prehospital care report is **FALSE?**

A. It documents the care that was provided.

B. It documents the patient's condition on arrival at the scene.

C. The documentation in the report cannot be used in a court of law.

D. The information serves to prove that the EMT-B has provided proper documentation.

33. What should you do first when the medical direction physician tells you to give a medication or treatment?

A. Do what the physician says.

B. Repeat the order back word for word.

C. Carefully write the order down in your run report.

D. Follow the order if you have time before arriving at the hospital.

34. The transfer of care officially occurs at the hospital during your formal oral report of the patient's condition. Name six elements of information that need to be reported to a hospital staff member.

35. List seven items of patient information that should be included in the minimum data set.

36. Name six functions of the prehospital care report.

37. Describe two types of report forms you may be using in EMS.

38. When the dispatcher notifies you of an incident, you will report in to dispatch a minimum of six times during the run. List these six times.

39. Using a copy of your local run report, complete it based on the following patient information and incident history.

Ken Smith is a 27-year-old athlete who, on his way back from a Colorado ski trip, drove his new sports car off an icy mountain road. The initial call was received by 9-1-1 at 1330 hours on February 12, 1995. Medic 917 was dispatched at 1331 hours and was en route at 1333 hours.

Medic 917 arrives on the scene at 1345 hours. EMTs John Keely and Valerie Summit find Ken lying inside the car upside down at the bottom of a ravine below a 50-foot cliff. He is unconscious but responds to painful stimuli. He is not moving his arms or legs. Peripheral pulses are present. There is no gross bleeding, although he has several lacerations about the head and face, an open femoral fracture on the right, and an open tibial fracture on the left. He has a pulse of 120/min, a blood pressure of 120/80 mm Hg, respirations of 30/min, and his pupils are equal and reactive to light.

The cervical spine is stabilized, and an extrication collar is applied. Ken is removed from the car, and traction and stabilization are applied to both lower extremities. He is then log rolled onto a long spine board. Oxygen at 15 L/min by mask is begun.

Patient assessment at this time shows multiple facial and scalp lacerations. There is no evidence of spinal fluid at the ears and nose. The pupils are equal and reactive to light. The chest is clear to auscultation. Respirations have dropped to 22/min and are less labored. The abdomen is rigid with no bowel sounds. There is questionable crepitus on compression of the pelvis. A medical alert necklace on Ken indicates he is a diabetic and allergic to penicillin. The vital signs taken at 1352 hours show a pulse of 140/min and a blood pressure of 80/60 mm Hg. A traction splint is applied to the right leg. Distal neurovascular status remains intact in both feet.

The patient is secured to the long spine board and transferred to the ambulance. Transport to General Hospital is begun at 1357 hours, arriving at 1408 hours. Vital signs and level of consciousness remain unchanged during transport.

General Pharmacology

Certain medications are authorized to be carried on the EMS unit. For each of the following medications, indicate whether it is routinely carried on the unit (A), or not carried (B).

1. _____ oxygen   A. routinely carried on the unit

2. _____ oral glucose   B. not carried on the unit

3. _____ prescribed inhaler

4. _____ nitroglycerin

5. _____ activated charcoal

6. _____ epinephrine

For each of the following descriptions, indicate whether it refers to a generic medication name (A), or a trade medication name (B).

7. _____ a simple form of   A. generic medication name
   the chemical name

8. _____ the name listed in the   B. trade medication name
   United States
   Pharmacopoeia

9. _____ the name used by the
   manufacturer in marketing
   the drug

10. _____ the name given to the drug
    before it becomes officially
    listed

For each of the terms in the left column, choose the appropriate definition in the right column. Each definition may be used once, more than once, or not at all.

11. _____ dose

12. _____ administration

13. _____ action

14. _____ side effect

A. how a drug is given

B. desired effects a drug has on a patient

C. the amount of the drug that is given

D. any actions of a drug other than those desired

Mark the following statements about medication administration T for true or F for false.

15. _____ A metered-dose inhaler is designed to deliver the same dose of medication each time it is used for inhalation.

16. _____ A small tablet that is designed to dissolve very easily is most useful when given sublingually.

17. _____ A medication that is absorbed sublingually will get into the blood more slowly than if it is swallowed.

18. _____ In emergency situations, it is best not to give medications that need to be swallowed.

19. _____ A contraindication is a situation where a drug should not be used because it may cause harm to the patient.

Mark the following statements about patient medication history T for true or F for false.

20. _____ When transferring care of a patient at the hospital, there is no need to report the patient's medication history to hospital personnel.

21. _____ Knowing something about a patient's medication history may help you assess a patient in an emergency situation.

22. Which of the following methods would be the best way to give a medication to treat a problem in the lungs and avoid side effects in other parts of the body?

A. Injection

B. Ingestion

C. Inhalation

D. Absorption

23. Why are certain medications, such as activated charcoal, authorized to be carried on the EMS unit?

24. List 10 common dosage forms for medications.

25. List three routes for injecting medication.

26. The EMT-B is authorized to assist a patient in giving what three medications if they have already been prescribed?

27. A patient with a prescription for nitroglycerin is experiencing chest pain. List two reasons why is it important to make sure the patient takes the medication.

28. A patient is having an asthma attack. What can a prescribed inhaler do?

29. What precautions should you take when giving oxygen to a patient?

30. Why does activated charcoal move through the digestive system quickly?

Respiratory Emergencies

For each of the terms in the left column, select the appropriate definition in the right column. Each definition may be used once, more than once, or not at all.

1. _____ dyspnea

2. _____ asthma

3. _____ croup

4. _____ bronchitis

5. _____ epiglottitis

6. _____ COPD

A. inflammation from an infection causing a partial upper airway obstruction and a barking cough

B. swelling of the glottis with airway obstruction

C. swelling of the flap over the larynx due to infection

D. irritation of the large air passages

E. irritation of the small air passages

F. airway obstruction due to muscle spasm and excessive mucus

G. fibrosis and constriction of the alveoli, preventing expansion

H. dilation and disruption of the airways and alveoli

I. shortness of breath

For each of the patient descriptions in the left column, select a term from the right column that would be the most likely cause of shortness of breath. Each term may be used once, more than once, or not at all.

7. _____ 2-year-old eating in a fast-food restaurant

8. _____ 15-year-old mowing the lawn and stung by a bee

9. _____ 65-year-old with a well-functioning tracheostomy

A. dust

B. hyperventilation

C. inhaled or aspirated foreign object

10. _____ 2-year-old with a runny nose and barking cough

11. _____ 20-year-old with dizziness and numbness of the fingers

D. diphtheria

E. croup

F. anaphylaxis

G. dysentery

H. COPD

Mark the following statements about breathing problems T for true or F for false.

12. _____ With labored breathing, exhalation is passive.

13. _____ Pneumonia is an infection of the lung.

14. _____ Hyperventilation is deep, slow breathing.

15. _____ Bronchitis can be caused by infection or irritants like smoke.

16. _____ Asthma is a disease only seen in children.

Mark the following statements about breathing patterns in infants and children T for true or F for false.

17. _____ Infants and children breathe slower than adults.

18. _____ Exhalation becomes active when infants and children have trouble breathing.

19. _____ A child has respirations of 25 to 50 breaths per minute.

20. _____ Nasal flaring is a sign of abnormal breathing.

Because a lack of oxygen affects all organs, there are many signs and symptoms of breathing problems. Mark the following signs and symptoms of breathing problems T for true or F for false.

21. _____ restlessness and anxiety

22. _____ decreased pulse rate

23. _____ changes in skin color

24. _____ quiet breathing

25. _____ ability to speak

26. _____ shallow, slow breathing

27. _____ abdominal breathing

28. _____ retractions

29. Which of the following is **NOT** a sign that an adult is breathing abnormally?

A. Pale skin

B. Cool, damp skin

C. Movement of the abdomen

D. Muscle retractions above the clavicles, between the ribs, and below the rib cage

30. Define respiration.

31. Sympathomimetic drugs mimic the hormone:

32. What action do beta agonists perform when they are inhaled?

33. List four conditions that can prevent the proper exchange of oxygen and carbon dioxide.

34. List five characteristics of normal breathing.

Cardiac Emergencies

For each of the terms in the left column, select the appropriate description about heart rhythm in the right column. Each description may be used once, more than once, or not at all.

1. _____ asystole

2. _____ arrhythmia

3. _____ tachycardia

4. _____ bradycardia

5. _____ ventricular fibrillation (VF)

A. rapid, regular heartbeat

B. abnormally slow, regular heartbeat

C. complete absence of heart activity

D. sudden irregularity of the heart rhythm

E. disorganized, ineffective quivering of the heart

For each of the terms in the left column, select the appropriate definition in the right column. Each definition may be used once, more than once, or not at all.

6. _____ artery

7. _____ femoral

8. _____ capillary

9. _____ carotid

10. _____ vein

11. _____ arteriole

12. _____ venule

13. _____ brachial

14. _____ radial

A. carries blood away from the heart to the rest of the body

B. small branch of an artery leading to the capillaries

C. connects arterioles to venules

D. small branch of a vein leading to the capillaries

E. carries blood back to the heart from the body

F. major artery of the neck

G. major artery of the thigh

H. major artery of the forearm

I. major artery of the upper arm

Mark the following statements about the electrical conduction system T for true or F for false.

15. _____ Specialized tissue capable of conducting electrical current runs through the heart.

16. _____ The electrical system remains unaffected if part of the heart does not receive enough oxygen.

17. _____ Premature ventricular contractions (PVCs) can occur when an injured part of the heart begins to fire off uncoordinated electrical impulses.

18. _____ Several PVCs close together produce a rhythm called ventricular tachycardia (VT).

19. _____ Ventricular fibrillation (VF) occurs when all detectable electrical activity in the heart stops.

Mark the following statements about nitroglycerin T for true or F for false.

20. _____ Nitroglycerin loses its potency after 5 years.

21. _____ Nitroglycerin helps relieve chest pain by dilating the coronary arteries.

22. _____ Nitroglycerin tablets may burn under the tongue or give the patient a headache.

23. _____ A patient with a nitroglycerin patch on the chest will not need defibrillation.

24. _____ Nitroglycerin relieves the pain of angina pectoris.

25. _____ Nitroglycerin can cause a fire if the patches are left on the chest during use of a defibrillator.

26. _____ The EMT-B may experience a decrease in blood pressure and a headache if the paste or spray comes into contact with the EMT-B's skin.

Mark the following statements about interruption of CPR T for true or F for false.

27. _____ CPR may be performed while shocks are delivered.

28. _____ No one should be touching the patient when the rhythm is being analyzed and when shocks are delivered.

29. _____ Chest compressions and artificial ventilations can continue while the rhythm is being analyzed.

30. _____ Defibrillation is less effective than CPR.

31. _____ CPR may be stopped up to 90 seconds if three shocks are necessary.

32. _____ If there is no pulse after three shocks, restart CPR for 1 minute.

Mark the following statements about AED standard operating procedures T for true or F for false.

33. _____ The patient should be transported when the pulse returns.

34. _____ The patient should be transported when three shocks are delivered.

35. _____ One EMT-B is able to operate the defibrillator and perform CPR.

36. _____ Rhythm analysis and defibrillation can be delayed until oxygen is hooked up.

37. _____ All contact with the patient must be avoided during rhythm analysis.

38. _____ The AED batteries should be checked once a week.

Mark the following statements about defibrillation T for true or F for false.

39. _____ It is proper to use an AED for a 10-year-old child who weighs 70 lb.

40. _____ The AED is able to analyze a patient's heart rhythm during transport in the ambulance.

41. _____ Always make sure that other people are not touching the patient when you press the shock button.

42. _____ An ambulance service must have written protocols to regularly check an AED.

43. _____ Ambulance personnel should get in the habit of verbalizing the sequence of events of the cardiac arrest for the voice recorder of the AED.

44. Angina may cause pain that begins in the chest and radiates to the:

A. jaw.

B. left leg.

C. right leg.

D. lower abdomen.

45. Which of the following is **NOT** a proper way to give nitroglycerin?

    A. A pill dissolved under the tongue

    B. A pill swallowed with a sip of water

    C. A spray inside the mouth or cheek

    D. A paste applied to the skin on the chest

46. If a nitroglycerin pill does not relieve pain after 5 minutes, you should:

    A. start CPR.

    B. give a second nitroglycerin pill.

    C. transport immediately since a myocardial infarction is likely.

    D. prepare for automated external defibrillation to slow the heart rate.

47. To prevent biological death, how many minutes do you have to start CPR or defibrillate the heart after ventricular fibrillation (VF) begins?

    A. 1

    B. 4

    C. 10

    D. 15

48. A semiautomatic defibrillator will:

    A. be very effective for asystole.

    B. deliver a shock on its own if needed.

    C. always shock the patient if applied to the chest.

    D. give a message if a shock is needed, but require that a button be pressed for the shock.

49. Which of the following sequences should you go through after giving a shock with a semiautomatic defibrillator?

A. Remove the pads and rapidly transport to the hospital.

B. Reanalyze after the first shock and give a second only if you receive approval from medical direction.

C. Reanalyze, give a second shock if advised by the machine; reanalyze, give a third shock if advised; restart CPR if there is no pulse.

D. Reanalyze, give a second shock if advised by the machine; reanalyze, give a third shock if advised; reanalyze, give a fourth and final shock if needed.

50. You arrive alone at the scene of a suspected myocardial infarction and find the patient unresponsive. There is no pulse or respirations. Your first response should be to:

A. give several respirations mouth-to-mouth or with a mask.

B. give a hard precordial thump to the midsternum using a clenched fist.

C. start chest compressions for one-rescuer CPR and call for help.

D. apply a semiautomatic defibrillator and analyze to see if a shock is needed.

51. List 10 signs and symptoms of ischemic heart disease.

52. Name and describe two types of automated external defibrillators.

53. Before the defibrillator starts heart rhythm analysis, there are 11 operational steps you must complete. List, in order, these steps.

54. On the accompanying diagram, label the vessels and chambers of the right side of the heart and explain the blood flow.

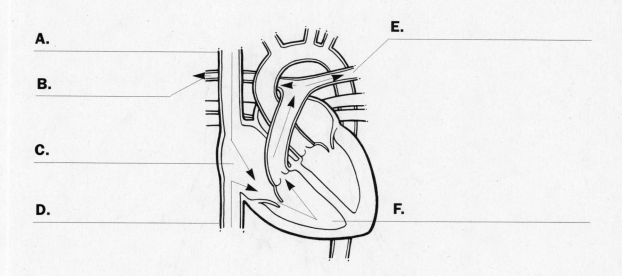

A.

B.

C.

D.

E.

F.

55. On the accompanying diagram, label the vessels and chambers of the left side of the heart and explain the blood flow.

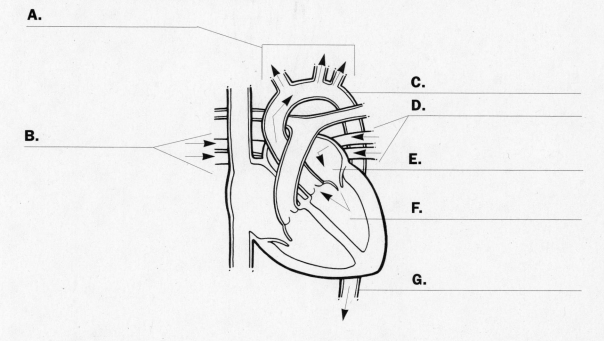

A.

B.

C.

D.

E.

F.

G.

56. On the accompanying diagram, label the major arteries of the body.

A.

B.

C.

D.

E.

F.

G.

H.

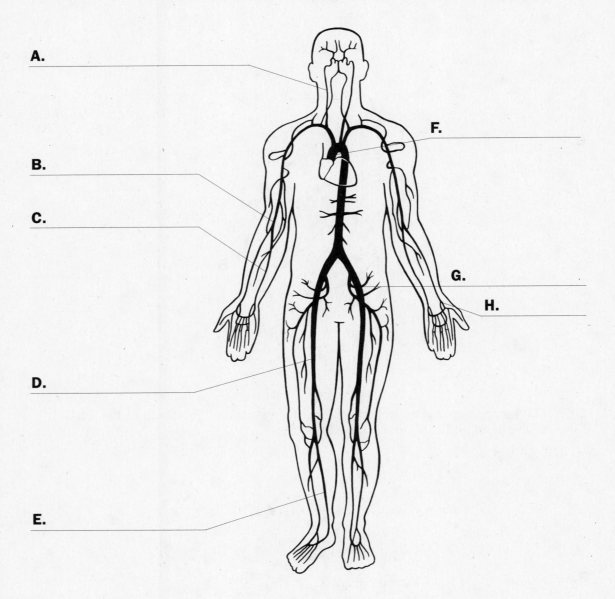

57. On the accompanying diagram, label the major veins of the body.

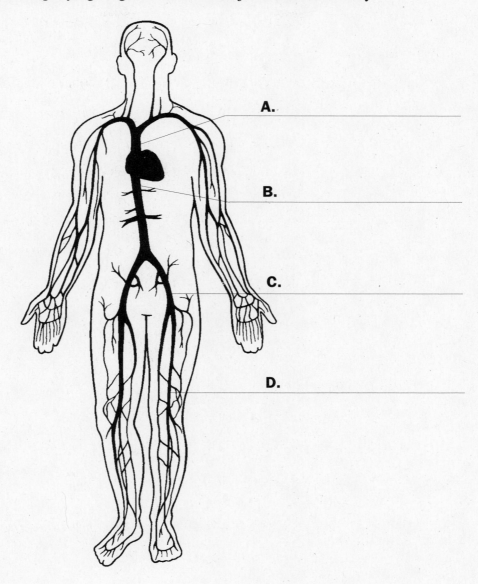

A.

B.

C.

D.

Diabetic Emergencies

Mark the following statements about diabetes T for true or F for false.

1. _____ Diabetes is caused by the lack of adequate amounts of insulin.

2. _____ Diabetics may require insulin to control their blood glucose.

3. _____ Glucose is a hormone that enables insulin to enter the cells of the body.

4. _____ Insulin is one of the basic sugars essential for cell metabolism in humans.

5. _____ Diabetes can cause kidney failure, blindness, and damage to blood vessels.

6. _____ Most children with diabetes are insulin dependent.

7. _____ Many adults with diabetes can control their blood glucose levels with diet alone.

8. _____ All diabetics can be cured by losing weight.

Mark the following statements about diabetic emergencies T for true or F for false.

9. _____ When patients use fat for energy, the fat waste products increase the amount of acid in the blood and tissue.

10. _____ The presence of acid waste products and frequent urination can affect the level of consciousness.

11. _____ The level of consciousness can be affected if a patient has not exercised enough.

12. _____ If blood glucose levels remain low, a patient may lose consciousness or have permanent brain damage.

13. _____ Signs and symptoms can develop quickly in children because their level of activity can exhaust their glucose levels.

14. _____ Diabetic emergencies can occur when a patient's blood glucose level gets too high or when it drops too low.

15. _____ Too much blood glucose does not directly affect a patient's level of consciousness.

16. _____ Changes in level of consciousness can occur if a patient overeats and then increases his or her insulin dose.

17. Which of the following is **NOT** a sign or symptom in a patient experiencing a diabetic emergency?

A. Hunger

B. Rapid pulse

C. Hot, dry skin

D. Intoxicated appearance

18. If you are unsure as to whether a patient has high or low blood glucose levels, you should:

A. give the patient a diet soft drink.

B. observe the patient to see what will happen.

C. always treat the patient as if the blood glucose is low.

D. always treat the patient as if the blood glucose is high.

19. Before giving a patient oral glucose, you should check to see if the patient can:

A. sit up.

B. swallow.

C. follow your directions.

D. tell you where he or she is.

20. What form does oral glucose come in?

A. Gel

B. Juice

C. Powder

D. Sugar cube

21. The level of consciousness is normally **NOT** affected if a patient has:

A. not eaten enough.

B. taken too much insulin.

C. exercised too vigorously.

D. had a diet soft drink with a meal.

22. Oral glucose gel acts to:

A. increase insulin levels.

B. increase blood glucose levels.

C. decrease insulin levels.

D. decrease blood glucose levels.

23. A 16-year-old boy who has diabetes is unresponsive. There are no obvious injuries, and his mother tells you that he has been fine except for a head cold for the last week. What is the most likely cause of his unresponsiveness?

A. Head injury

B. Low blood glucose levels

C. Kidney failure

D. Drug overdose

24. Most diabetics used to check their urine daily for the presence of glucose and acetone. What type of kit is now available that gives a more direct and current assessment of their condition?

25. Briefly define and explain the role of insulin in normal metabolism.

26. What does it mean when a patient is said to be an insulin-dependent diabetic?

27. What four questions should you ask the patient or the family at the scene of a diabetic emergency?

28. List two ways for you to confirm if an unconscious patient has diabetes.

29. What are two trade names for oral glucose?

30. What is the only contraindication to giving oral glucose to a patient experiencing a diabetic emergency?

Allergies and Poisoning

For each of the terms in the left column, select the appropriate definition in the right column. Each definition may be used once, more than once, or not at all.

1. _____ urticaria (hives)

2. _____ stridor

3. _____ wheezing

4. _____ ingestion

5. _____ poison

6. _____ toxin

7. _____ allergens

A. substances that cause allergic reactions

B. taking a substance by mouth

C. noisy respirations resulting from a large partial blockage of the upper airway

D. substance whose chemical action could damage structures or impair function when introduced into the body in small amounts

E. poison or harmful substance, produced by bacteria, animals, or plants

F. audible high-pitched breath sound usually resulting from a small airway blockage

G. small areas of generalized itching, burning, and the development of multiple raised, reddened areas on the skin

H. reaction that occurs when the body has an extreme immune response to an agent

Mark the following statements about allergic reactions T for true or F for false.

8. _____ Life-threatening allergic reactions can occur in response to almost any substance that a patient may encounter.

9. _____ Shock and respiratory failure always occur after an allergic reaction.

10. _____ An allergic reaction occurs when the body has an immune response to a substance.

11. _____ You should always examine the respiratory system when you suspect an allergic reaction.

12. _____ Hives can only be brought on by skin contact with a substance.

Mark the following statements about poisoning T for true or F for false.

13. _____ A substance is a poison regardless of whether it is swallowed, inhaled, injected, or absorbed.

14. _____ Only very large amounts of poisonous substances can cause injury or death.

15. _____ About 80% of all poisonings involve swallowed poisons.

16. _____ Among adults, contaminated foods are the most commonly ingested poisons.

17. _____ A clue to an ingested poison is the patient having an unusual breath odor.

18. _____ Chlorine, when inhaled, produces profound hypoxia without irritating or damaging the lungs.

Mark the following statements about activated charcoal T for true or F for false.

19. _____ Activated charcoal should never be used in an unconscious patient.

20. _____ Children like to drink activated charcoal.

21. _____ Shaking the activated charcoal mixture makes it work less well.

22. _____ The major side effect of ingesting activated charcoal is black stools.

23. The first thing you should do when you think your patient is having an allergic reaction is to:

A. begin CPR.

B. start an IV.

C. give oxygen.

D. apply a pneumatic antishock garment (PASG).

24. Your patient may be carrying a drug kit to combat allergic reactions. The drug in this kit is called:

A. calcium.

B. atropine.

C. epinephrine.

D. sodium bicarbonate.

25. What substance in the body may contribute to an allergic reaction?

A. Bile

B. Lymph

C. Benedryl

D. Histamine

26. Common side effects of epinephrine include:

A. headache, cyanosis, and hunger.

B. headache, chest pain, and nausea.

C. hives, shortness of breath, and pallor.

D. hives, low blood pressure, and a feeling of calmness.

27. After a patient has used an auto-injector, you should:

A. call 9-1-1 for help.

B. give a second dose.

C. reassess the patient's vital signs.

D. place a tourniquet above the injection site.

28. After providing care for a patient with an allergic reaction, you should:

A. refer the patient to a clinic.

B. advise the patient to see a doctor.

C. provide rapid transport to the hospital.

D. suggest the patient buy an auto-injector.

29. The general treatment of a poisoned patient is to:

A. start an IV.

B. induce vomiting.

C. give activated charcoal.

D. assess and maintain the patient's ABCD.

30. The usual adult dose of activated charcoal is:

A.   5 to 10 g.

B.   10 to 20 g.

C.   25 to 50 g.

D. 100 to 150 g.

31. An immediate treatment of inhaled poisons is to:

A. induce vomiting.

B. give activated charcoal.

C. await the arrival of the HazMat team.

D. move the patient into the fresh air when safe.

32. A common sign that you will see following absorption of a poison through the skin is:

A. vomiting.

B. nasal stuffiness.

C. tearing of the eyes.

D. intense burning or itching.

33. How does activated charcoal work to counteract ingested poison?

34. List four stimuli that most often cause allergic reactions.

35. List four routes of contact for poisoning.

36. List three types of poisoning by injection.

Environmental Emergencies

CHAPTER · CHAPTER · CHAPTER **19**

In the left column, descriptions of the ways heat is lost are listed. For each description, select the most appropriate term on the right. Each term may be used once, more than once, or not at all.

1. _____ normal breathing   A. radiation

2. _____ sweating   B. convection

3. _____ bare foot touching a cold floor   C. conduction

4. _____ conversion of a liquid to a gas   D. respiration

5. _____ loss of heat through air passing over the body   E. evaporation

6. _____ loss of heat from one solid body to another

7. _____ loss of heat from the body to a colder environment

8. _____ swimmer coming from water to land

9. _____ person working in an air-conditioned office

10. _____ tongue touching ice cream

For each of the terms in the left column, select the appropriate definition in the right column. Each definition may be used once, more than once, or not at all.

11. _____ hypothermia   A. deposit of venom into a wound

12. _____ hyperthermia   B. death from suffocation by submersion in water

13. _____ shivering   C. a condition in which the internal body temperature drops below 95°F

14. _____ superficial cold injury   D. tissues are frozen

15. _____ deep cold injury

E. a condition in which the body gains or retains more heat than it loses

16. _____ drowning

F. an attempt to generate more heat through muscular activity

17. _____ diving reflex

G. freezing of the skin, but not the deeper tissues

18. _____ envenomation

H. slowing of the heart rate caused by submersion in cold water

Mark the following statements about environmental emergencies T for true or F for false.

19. _____ The normal body temperature is 98.6°F (37.0°C).

20. _____ To assess the skin temperature in a patient experiencing a generalized cold emergency, you should feel the patient's forehead.

21. _____ All patients with severe, multiple injuries are likely to have some degree of hypothermia.

22. _____ Mild hypothermia occurs when the core temperature drops to 85°F.

23. _____ The body's most efficient heat regulating mechanisms are sweating and dilation of skin blood vessels.

24. _____ People who are at greatest risk for heat illnesses are the elderly and children.

25. _____ The signs and symptoms of exposure to heat can include moist, pale skin.

26. _____ Cold should not be applied to snake bites.

27. _____ The strongest stimulus for breathing is an elevation of oxygen in the blood.

28. _____ Immediate bradycardia after jumping in cold water is called the diving reflex.

29. _____ The signs and symptoms of exposure to heat can include hot, dry skin.

30. _____ A bee stinger should be removed with tweezers.

31. A patient with a core temperature between 90° and 95°F is usually:

A. dizzy.

B. lethargic.

C. shivering.

D. poorly coordinated.

32. You have been called to the scene of a possible drowning. A 32-year-old woman has been underwater for an extended period of time. Your first step should be to:

A. assess the patient's pulse.

B. perform the Heimlich maneuver.

C. begin mouth-to-mask ventilation.

D. check for hyperthermia

33. Which of the following snakes is **NOT** poisonous?

A. Coral

B. Python

C. Copperhead

D. Cottonmouth

34. Which of the following is **NOT** an appropriate treatment for a snake bite?

A. Splint the extremity.

B. Apply cold to the bite.

C. Keep the patient supine.

D. Apply venous tourniquets with approval from medical control.

35. With vigorous exercise, the body can lose more than _____ liter(s) of sweat per hour.

36. State the basic rule of water rescue.

37. List two basic steps to manage hypothermia.

38. List four main predisposing factors for a cold emergency.

39. List three environmental factors that determine the severity of a local cold injury.

Behavioral Emergencies

For each of the terms in the left column, select the appropriate description in the right column. Each description may be used once, more than once, or not at all.

1. _____ paranoia

2. _____ depression

3. _____ behavior

4. _____ mania

5. _____ disruptive behavior

6. _____ suicidal act

7. _____ behavioral emergency

A. manner in which a person acts

B. a state in which the patient may believe that people are plotting to harm or kill him or her

C. a situation in which the patient acts abnormally in a way that is unacceptable or intolerable to the patient, family, or community

D. a state in which the patient may not want to do anything, and may not cooperate or answer questions

E. a state in which the patient may be severely agitated, speaking rapidly, and usually not finishing a sentence or a complete thought

F. a state in which a patient may be threatening to kill himself or herself or may have already made an attempt

G. behavior that puts the patient or others in danger or delays treatment

Mark the following statements about behavioral emergencies T for true or F for false.

8. _____ When a patient has to be restrained, he or she should be placed on a stretcher in a facedown position that allows for adequate ventilation and secured with multiple straps.

9. _____ It is important to avoid looking directly at the patient when dealing with behavioral emergencies.

10. _____ When transporting a patient with a behavioral problem, it is important to have a witness in attendance.

11. _____ When a patient has to be restrained, it should be done by the EMT-B, not the police, to avoid possibly injuring the patient.

12. _____ Low blood glucose or a lack of oxygen can cause behavioral changes.

13. _____ The majority of patients with organic brain syndrome are elderly.

14. _____ People who are alcoholics, depressed, or alone, without support, are at risk for suicide.

15. _____ Never turn your back on a disturbed patient.

16. _____ If a patient presents a threat to self or others, you can legally restrain the patient against his or her will.

17. _____ A disturbed patient should always be transported with restraints.

18. _____ Police-type handcuffs should be used to restrain a patient.

19. _____ When restraining a patient, you should try to have four law enforcement officers present to help.

20. _____ You can relax when a combative patient suddenly becomes calm and cooperative.

21. _____ Abnormal behavior caused by a head injury or stroke can occur 2 to 3 weeks after the injury.

22. Which of the following steps is **NOT** appropriate when treating a disturbed patient?

A. Keep your movements slow and deliberate.

B. Use words and body language to keep the patient calm.

C. Tell the patient what you are going to do before you do it.

D. Leave the patient alone for a few minutes so he or she can collect his or her thoughts.

23. The proper sequence of emergency medical care for behavioral emergencies is:

A. patient assessment, calm the patient, scene size-up, and transport the patient.

B. calm the patient, patient assessment, scene size-up, and transport the patient.

C. scene size-up, patient assessment, calm the patient, and transport the patient.

D. scene size-up, calm the patient, patient assessment, and transport the patient.

24. Before restraining a patient, you should:

A. consult with family members.

B. ask the patient for permission.

C. maintain close physical contact to calm him or her down.

D. consult medical control and contact law enforcement.

25. You are caring for a patient experiencing a behavioral emergency. As you question the patient and family to try and determine the cause, which of the following questions is **NOT** considered appropriate?

A. Has there been a head injury?

B. Has the patient been ill lately?

C. Has there been a history of similar behavior?

D. Has any close relative had a history of psychiatric illness?

26. List five signs of depression that often accompany suicide attempts.

27. List four signs or symptoms of psychiatric disorders.

28. List four factors to consider about a patient when deciding how much force is necessary to keep the patient from injuring himself, herself, or others.

29. When a patient's family reports a significant personality change, consider the possibility of a:

30. When dealing with an emotionally disturbed patient, the best legal situation is to obtain:

Obstetrics and Gynecology

For each of the terms in the left column, select the most appropriate definition in the right column. Each definition may be used once, more than once, or not at all.

1. _____ cervix

    A. the hollow organ inside the female pelvis where the fetus grows

2. _____ meconium

    B. a fluid-filled, bag-like membrane that grows around the developing fetus, inside the uterus

3. _____ placenta

    C. sterile fecal material released from the baby's bowels before birth

4. _____ amniotic sac

    D. the opening of the uterus

5. _____ fetus

    E. the tissue that connects the placenta with the fetus

6. _____ miscarriage

    F. two soft areas on the baby's head

7. _____ birth canal

    G. the outermost part of a woman's reproductive system

8. _____ uterus

    H. the developing baby in the uterus

9. _____ umbilical cord

    I. delivery of the fetus and placenta before 20 weeks gestation, for any reason

10. _____ vagina

    J. the vagina and lower part of the uterus

    K. afterbirth that develops on the wall of the uterus and is connected to the fetus by the umbilical cord

Mark the following statements about the delivery process T for true or F for false.

11. _____ A small mucous plug from the cervix that comes out of the vagina, often at the beginning of labor, is called a bloody show.

12. _____ Crowning occurs when the baby's head obstructs the birth canal, preventing normal delivery.

13. _____ Labor begins with the rupture of the amniotic membranes and ends with the delivery of the baby's head.

14. _____ A woman who is having her first baby is called a multigravida.

15. _____ Once labor has begun, you can slow down or stop it by holding the patient's legs together.

16. _____ Once the baby is born, the umbilical cord is of no further use to either the mother or the baby.

17. _____ Delivery of the buttocks before the baby's head is called a breech delivery.

18. _____ After delivery, the baby should be kept at the same level as the mother's vagina until the cord is cut.

19. _____ The placenta and cord should be put into a plastic bag and discarded after delivery.

20. _____ Once the cord has been cut, the end coming from the baby should be tied with string or twine.

21. _____ You should never try to pull the baby's head out during a breech delivery.

22. _____ A limb presentation occurs when the baby's arm, leg, or foot is emerging from the vagina first.

23. Which of the following statements about multiple births is **FALSE?**

A. Twins are usually smaller than single babies.

B. Multiple births never have more than one placenta.

C. The second baby may deliver before or after the first placenta.

D. Twins should be suspected if the mother's abdomen remains fairly large after the birth.

24. You are called to see a patient who is delivering. The baby's head is out and the cord is wrapped around the neck. You should:

A. give the baby oxygen.

B. pull on the baby to speed up the delivery.

C. try to slip the cord over the baby's shoulder.

D. hold the baby in place and provide rapid transport.

25. If the umbilical cord delivers before the baby, you should:

A. cover it with a dressing and transport.

B. cut it so the ends can retract out of the way.

C. push the cord back into the mother.

D. push the baby's head up using your sterile gloved hand in the vagina.

26. As the head is delivering during a breech presentation, you should put your gloved finger into the mother's vagina to:

A. check the baby's pulse.

B. assess dilation of the cervix.

C. clear and protect the baby's airway.

D. push the baby back up and slow delivery until arrival at the hospital.

27. As a mother is delivering her baby, you note meconium staining. You should:

A. wash off the baby.

B. consider intubating the baby to clear the airway.

C. wait for the placenta to deliver before starting treatment.

D. suction the mouth and oropharynx before stimulating the baby.

28. Which of the following statements about premature infants is true?

A. Premature babies do not usually require resuscitation.

B. A premature baby's head is proportionately smaller compared with the rest of its body.

C. A baby that weighs less than $5 \frac{1}{2}$ lb at birth is considered premature.

D. A baby that delivers before 9 months gestation is considered premature.

29. Describe the two ways to give chest compressions to a baby.

30. List three conditions in which you may have to consider assisting with a delivery at the scene.

31. The onset of labor is the beginning of the delivery process. List three signs that indicate the beginning of labor.

32. Twenty minutes after delivery of a normal-appearing baby, the placenta has still not delivered. List two steps that you should take next before transporting the mother to the hospital.

For each of the terms in the left column, select the most appropriate definition in the right column. Each definition may be used once, more than once, or not at all.

1. _____ perfusion

A. bleeding

2. _____ shock

B. formation of clots to plug openings in injured blood vessels and stop blood flow

3. _____ epistaxis

C. a condition in which the circulatory system fails to provide sufficient circulation so that every body part can perform its function

4. _____ coagulation

D. a condition in which low blood volume, due to massive internal or external bleeding, results in inadequate perfusion

5. _____ hypovolemic shock

E. nosebleed

6. _____ hemorrhage

F. a condition where the blood lacks one or more normal clotting factors

7. _____ hypoperfusion

G. circulation of blood within an organ or tissue in adequate amounts to meet the cells' current needs

For each of the terms in the left column, select the most appropriate definition in the right column. Each definition may be used once, more than once, or not at all.

8. _____ hematuria

A. bleeding from the rectum

9. _____ hemoptysis

B. bright red or dark red vomited blood

10. _____ hematochezia

C. blood in the urine

11. _____ coffee grounds vomitus

D. dark, foul-smelling tarry stools containing digested blood

12. _____ melena

E. bright red blood that has been coughed up

13. _____ hematemesis

F. blood that has been partially digested

Mark the following statements about the cardiovascular system T for true or F for false.

14. _____ Carbon monoxide is carried away from the cells by the veins.

15. _____ Shock occurs when oxygen and nutrients cannot get to the body's cells and tissues and waste products cannot be removed.

16. _____ Arteries are the smallest vessels that carry oxygen to the individual cells of the body.

17. _____ Capillaries are approximately the same size as red blood cells.

18. _____ Capillaries are rigid tubes that do not have the ability to constrict and dilate.

19. _____ An adult has approximately 6 L of blood.

20. _____ Venous blood tends to spurt and is difficult to manage.

21. _____ Over time and within limits, the body adapts to a slow and steady blood loss.

Mark the following statements about bleeding and shock T for true or F for false.

22. _____ You can control internal bleeding easily in the field.

23. _____ Bleeding is the most common cause of shock after trauma.

24. _____ Ecchymosis means bruising.

25. _____ A mass of blood in the soft tissues beneath the skin is called a hematoma.

26. _____ Severe internal bleeding from trauma requires field stabilization prior to transport.

27. Which of the following structures requires a constant blood flow to live?

A. Skin

B. Brain

C. Muscle

D. Gastrointestinal tract

28. A bleeding patient exposes you to potentially infectious body fluids. Under BSI, which of the following protective devices are necessary in all situations?

A. Goggles and mask

B. Gloves and eye protection

C. Gloves, shirt, and shoe covers

D. Mask, gown, and shoe covers

29. You are at the most risk for acquiring an infection when:

A. a patient coughs on you.

B. a patient vomits on your skin.

C. you have an open sore or cut.

D. you are in the back of the ambulance with a patient.

30. In most cases of external hemorrhage, bleeding usually stops on its own within how many minutes?

A.   2 to 5

B.   6 to 10

C. 11 to 16

D. 17 to 20

31. Bleeding usually stops on its own as a result of:

A. a clot being formed.

B. the skin warming up.

C. the muscle constricting.

D. the patient running out of blood.

32. Which of the following statements about the use of an air splint is **FALSE?**

A. It acts like a pressure bandage.

B. It is appropriate for use on pelvic fractures.

C. It can control the bleeding associated with severe soft tissue injuries.

D. Circulation in the distal extremity needs to be monitored after applying an air splint.

33. You have applied a pneumatic antishock garment (PASG) on your patient. Which of the following do you need to monitor constantly during transport?

A. The air pressure in the suit

B. The patient's blood pressure

C. The patient's pupil reactivity

D. The patient's neurologic status

34. In which of the following circumstances should you avoid using a pneumatic antishock garment (PASG)?

A. Pelvic fracture

B. Groin injuries

C. Proximal femur fracture

D. Shock due to internal bleeding

35. A tourniquet should be applied only when:

A. the bleeding has stopped.

B. the bleeding is dark red and oozes steadily but slowly.

C. both extremities have been injured.

D. you cannot control the bleeding from an extremity's major vessel any other way.

36. List four steps that you can take at the scene to control epistaxis.

37. List three basic causes of shock.

38. List the three most commonly used methods to control external bleeding.

39. List nine signs and symptoms of early (compensated) shock.

40. Next to the body parts listed below, name an activity that creates a need for high blood flow to the organ.

	Body Part	Activity
1.	Muscles	
2.	Gastrointestinal tract	

Soft Tissue Injuries

For each of the descriptions in the left column, select the appropriate type of injury or wound in the right column. Each injury or wound type may be used once, more than once, or not at all.

1. _____ gunshot wound   A. abrasion

2. _____ flap of skin   B. laceration

3. _____ stab wound   C. hemothorax

4. _____ air around the lungs   D. penetrating wound

5. _____ road rash   E. avulsion

6. _____ razor cut   F. evisceration

7. _____ skinned knee   G. pneumothorax

8. _____ splinter

9. _____ exposed intestines

10. _____ blood inside the chest

11. _____ amputated ear

Mark the following statements about burns T for true or F for false.

12. _____ Partial-thickness burns involve the epidermis and some portion of the dermis.

13. _____ Blisters are commonly seen with superficial burns.

14. _____ Severe burns are usually a combination of superficial, partial-thickness, and full-thickness burns.

15. _____ The Rule of Nines allows you to estimate the percentage of body surface area that has been burned.

16. _____ Two factors, depth and extent, are critical in assessing the severity of a burn.

17. _____ Your first responsibility with a burn patient is to stop the burning process.

18. _____ Burned areas should be immersed in cool water for up to 30 minutes.

19. _____ Electrical burns are always more severe than the external signs indicate.

Mark the following statements about dressings and bandaging T for true or F for false.

20. _____ The universal dressing is ideal for covering large open wounds.

21. _____ Occlusive dressings are usually made of Vaseline gauze, aluminum foil, or plastic.

22. _____ Gauze pads prevent air and liquids from entering or exiting a wound.

23. _____ Elastic bandages can be used to secure dressings.

24. _____ Soft roller bandages are slightly elastic and the layers adhere somewhat to one another.

25. What layer of the skin is tough and watertight?

A. Muscle

B. Dermis

C. Epidermis

D. Subcutaneous tissue

26. The only condition under which you should try to remove an impaled object is when:

A. there is bleeding.

B. the object is longer than 1'.

C. the object is embedded in the skull.

D. the cheek is impaled and breathing is obstructed.

27. A closed injury is an injury in which there is no:

A. pain.

B. bruising.

C. bleeding.

D. break in the skin or mucous membrane.

28. Which of the following statements about an avulsion is **FALSE?**

A. There is usually little or no bleeding.

B. An avulsion can be completely unattached or hang as a flap.

C. Avulsed tissues ordinarily separate between the subcutaneous tissue and fascia.

D. If an avulsion is complete, the tissue should be wrapped in sterile gauze and brought to the emergency department.

29. Bleeding of an open wound is best controlled by applying:

A. ice.

B. water to flush the wound.

C. a tourniquet.

D. a dry, sterile compression dressing.

30. List three primary functions of dressings and bandaging.

31. List three classifications of burns.

32. List five factors that will help you determine the severity of a burn.

33. ICES is an acronym you can think of when you are called to treat a closed soft tissue injury. What word does each letter represent?

34. Name two dangers specifically associated with electrical burns.

35. List six steps to care for an open soft tissue injury.

36. Label the specialized structures of the skin on the accompanying diagram.

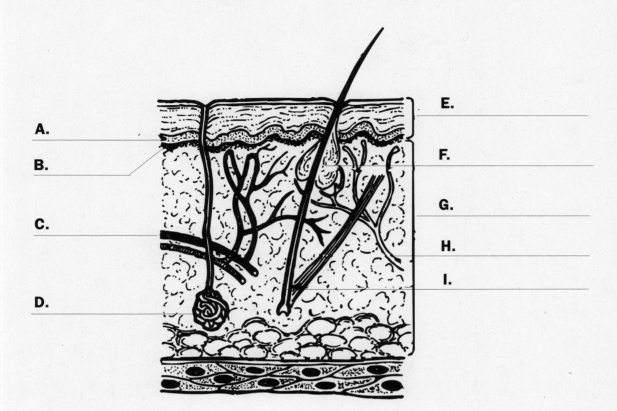

A.

B.

C.

D.

E.

F.

G.

H.

I.

37. On the accompanying Rule of Nines diagram, place the correct percentage on each body area.

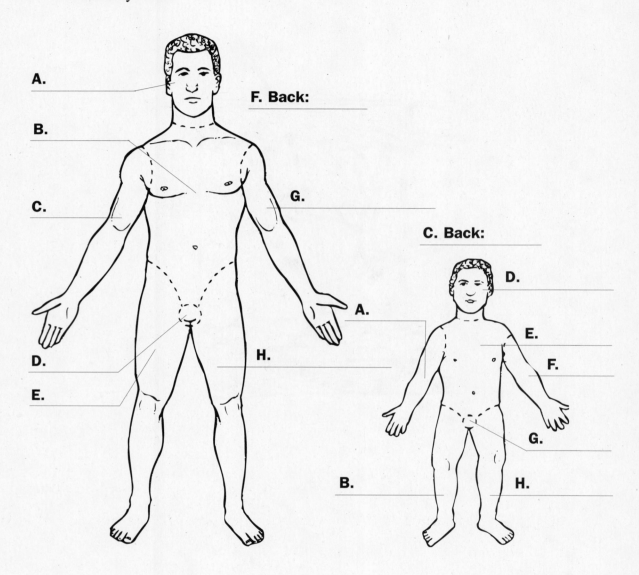

A.

B.

C.

D.

E.

F. Back: _____

G.

H.

A.

C. Back: _____

D.

E.

F.

G.

B. _____

H. _____

Musculoskeletal Care

For each of the terms in the left column, select the most appropriate definition in the right column. Each definition may be used once, more than once, or not at all.

1. _____ joint

A. a thin layer of cartilage, covering the articular surface of bones in synovial joints

2. _____ tendon

B. any fracture in which the skin has not been broken by the bone ends, and there is no wound anywhere near the injury site

3. _____ closed fracture

C. the act of exerting a pulling force on a structure

4. _____ point tenderness

D. any injury that makes the limb appear in an unnatural position

5. _____ ligament

E. any break in the bone in which the overlying skin has been damaged as well

6. _____ displaced fracture

F. a band of fibrous tissue that connects bones to bones

7. _____ articular cartilage

G. a tough, rope-like cord of fibrous tissue that attaches a skeletal muscle to a bone

8. _____ open fracture

H. tenderness sharply localized at the site of the injury

I. the place where two bones come in contact

Mark the following statements about splinting and traction T for true or F for false.

9. _____ All extremity injuries should be splinted before moving a patient, unless the patient's life is in immediate danger.

10. _____ Splinting reduces pain and prevents the motion of bone fragments.

11. _____ You should use traction to reduce a fracture and force all bone fragments back into alignment.

12. _____ The amount of pull needed to align a limb rarely exceeds 25 lb.

13. _____ When applying traction, the direction of pull is always along the long axis of the limb.

14. _____ Cover wounds with a dry, sterile dressing before applying a splint.

15. _____ When splinting a fracture, you should be careful to immobilize only the joint above the injury site.

Mark the following statements about evaluating neurologic function T for true or F for false.

16. _____ One of the steps of the neurologic examination is to palpate the pulse distal to the point of injury.

17. _____ When you assess capillary refill, the nail bed should return to a pink color in 5 seconds.

18. _____ Assessment of neurologic function should be repeated every 15 minutes until the patient arrives at the hospital.

19. _____ A patient's ability to sense light touch in the fingers or toes distal to the injury site is a good indication that the nerve supply is intact.

20. _____ A CMS evaluation can be performed when the patient is unconscious.

21. Which of the following statements about skeletal muscle is true?

A. It is involuntary muscle.

B. It controls internal functions of the body.

C. It has no direct attachments to the skeleton.

D. It forms the major muscle mass of the body.

22. The first step in the evaluation of a patient with an injured limb is to:

A. splint the injured limb.

B. cover all open wounds.

C. transport the patient to the emergency department.

D. perform an initial assessment and stabilize the patient's ABCD.

23. Most skeletal muscles are attached directly to bone by:

A. muscle.

B. tendons.

C. cartilage.

D. ligaments.

24. Which of the following is **NOT** a function of the skeleton?

A. Gives form to the body

B. Allows body movement

C. Produces white blood cells

D. Protects vital internal organs

25. Which of the following statements about pneumatic splints is **FALSE?**

A. Air splints provide uniform contact.

B. Air splints should always be inflated by mouth.

C. With temperature changes, the air pressure in the splint will vary.

D. Air splints can be used on injuries above the elbow and above the knee.

26. You are evaluating a painful, swollen, deformed limb and make the decision to apply traction. The patient strongly resists your attempts to apply traction. You should:

A. apply ice and transport the patient.

B. stop temporarily and then try again.

C. splint the limb in the deformed position.

D. continue your attempts while your partner restrains the patient.

27. List the proper sequence of steps (1 to 6) taken by two EMT-Bs in the application of a nonzippered air splint. Place the appropriate number next to each lettered step.

A.____ EMT-B #2 supports the injured limb.

B.____ EMT-B #2 inflates the splint by mouth.

C.____ EMT-B #1 applies gentle traction while sliding the splint onto the injured limb.

D.____ EMT-B #1 tests the air pressure.

E.____ EMT-B #1 checks and records the distal neurologic function.

F.____ EMT-B #1 places his or her arm through the splint and grasps the injured limb.

28. List five conditions where traction splints should **NOT** be used.

29. Define osteoporosis.

30. List six signs and symptoms of a displaced joint.

31. Name three types of splints.

32. Deformity is one sign of bone and joint injuries. List seven other signs.

33. List five hazards associated with improper splinting.

Injuries to the
Head and Spine

For each of the terms in the left column, select the most appropriate description in the right column. Each description may be used once, more than once, or not at all.

1. _____ autonomic nervous sytem

A. the part of the central nervous system that controls virtually all the functions that are absolutely necessary for life

2. _____ central nervous system

B. swelling of the brain

3. _____ distraction

C. three distinct layers of tissue that surround and protect the brain and the spinal cord within the skull and the spinal canal

4. _____ cerebral edema

D. the part of the nervous system that regulates functions that are not controlled by conscious will

5. _____ connecting nerves

E. the part of the brain that coordinates body movements

6. _____ involuntary nervous sytem

F. when the spine is pulled along its length

7. _____ brain stem

G. the brain and spinal cord

8. _____ intervertebral disk

H. the part of the nervous system that regulates our voluntary activities

9. _____ meninges

I. nerves that connect the motor and sensory nerves

10. _____ somatic nervous system

J. cushion that lies between the vertebrae

For each of the activities in the left column, select the appropriate type of nerve that controls it in the right column. Each type may be used once, more than once, or not at all.

11. _____ breathing

A. reflex

12. _____ knee jerk

B. involuntary

13. _____ writing

C. voluntary

14. _____ sweating

15. _____ withdrawal from pain

16. _____ heartbeat

17. _____ walking

Mark the following statements about the nervous system T for true or F for false.

18. _____ The somatic nervous system allows the brain to interpret the sensory information it receives from the peripheral nerves.

19. _____ If a sensory nerve in the reflex arc detects an irritating stimulus, it will bypass the motor nerve and send a message directly to the brain.

20. _____ Voluntary activities are those actions we perform unconsciously.

21. _____ The autonomic nervous system is composed of the sympathetic nervous system and the parasympathetic nervous system.

22. _____ The parasympathetic nervous system reacts to stress with the "fight or flight" response whenever it is confronted with a threatening situation.

23. You are caring for a patient with a suspected head injury. High-flow oxygen should be given:

A. when cyanosis develops.

B. when the patient is unconscious.

C. when respiratory distress is noted.

D. as soon as the airway is secured.

24. An 8-year-old girl has been injured in a motor vehicle accident and is unconscious. The cervical collar that you have available is too large. What steps should you take to immobilize the patient's head and spine?

A. Use the collar and make it fit as well as possible.

B. Use the collar and tape her head to the spine board.

C. Do not use the collar and place the patient on her left side.

D. While providing continuous manual support, tape a rolled towel to the spine board around the patient's head.

25. The most important first step in caring for a patient with a head injury is to:

A. control bleeding.

B. stabilize the spine.

C. establish an airway.

D. monitor respirations.

26. Which of the following is **NOT** a reason for removing a helmet?

A. Cardiac arrest

B. Warm weather conditions

C. Inability to assess the airway

D. Poorly fitting helmet that allows excessive head movement

27. What percentage of unconscious head injury patients must be suspected of having a cervical spine injury?

A. 20%

B. 50%

C. 80%

D. 100%

28. Which of the following statements about manual support of the head in a patient with a cervical spine injury is true?

A. It should not be applied if a cervical collar is to be used.

B. It should not be applied at all because the hands create additional movement.

C. It must be maintained until the cervical collar is securely in place.

D. It must be maintained until the patient is secured to a backboard and the head is immobilized.

29. There has been a motor vehicle accident where an infant in a car seat has possible spinal injuries. Your best course of action should be to:

    A. immobilize the infant in the car seat, if possible.

    B. remove the infant from the car seat and apply a cervical collar.

    C. remove the infant from the car seat and immobilize him or her on a long spine board.

    D. remove the entire car seat with the infant in it from the vehicle and further assess the possible spinal injury.

30. Describe the eyes forward position.

31. Manual in-line immobilization is the hallmark of care for patients believed to have a spinal cord injury. List four circumstances where this procedure should **NOT** be used.

32. List five questions you should ask a patient when assessing for possible spinal injuries.

33. List three kinds of intracranial hematomas and where they occur.

34. On the accompanying diagram, label the structures of the brain.

A.

B.

C.

D.

E.

F.

G.

H.

I.

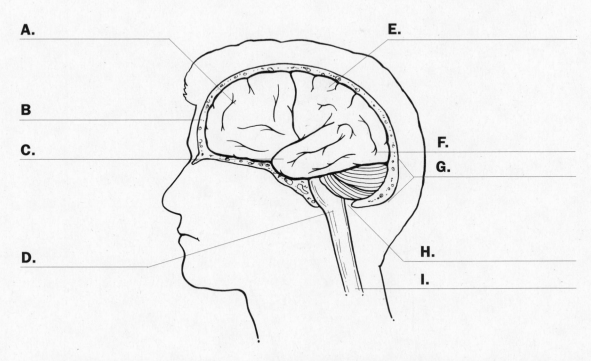

35. On the accompanying diagram, label the protective structures of the nervous system.

A.

B.

C.

D.

E.

F.

G.

H.

I.

J.

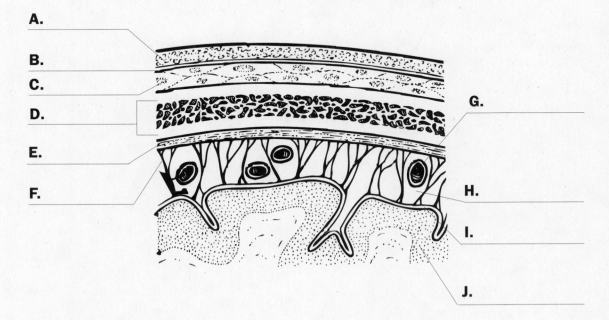

36. On the accompanying diagram, label the five sections of the spine.

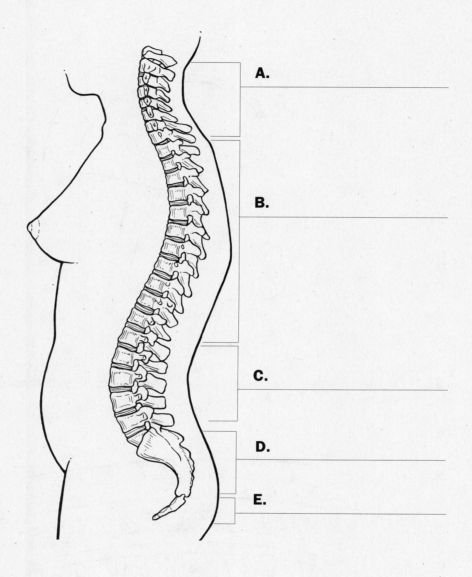

A. _____

B. _____

C. _____

D. _____

E. _____

Infants and Children

For each of the terms in the left column, select the most appropriate description in the right column. Each description may be used once, more than once, or not at all.

1. _____ neonate

2. _____ pediatrics

3. _____ child abuse

4. _____ sudden infant death syndrome (SIDS)

5. _____ meningitis

6. _____ dehydration

A. loss of water from the tissues of the body

B. medical practice devoted to the care of children up to age 18

C. any improper or excessive action that injures or harms a child or infant

D. death from unknown cause occurring during sleep in an otherwise healthy infant

E. a newborn infant

F. an inflammation of the meningeal coverings of the brain and spinal cord caused by either a virus or a bacterium

Mark the following statements about pediatric patients T for true or F for false.

7. _____ From birth until the age of 1 year, a child is regarded as a neonate.

8. _____ Children between the ages of 1 and 3 years are considered toddlers.

9. _____ For children older than 5 years, adult basic airway techniques are effective.

10. _____ Children ages 6 to 12 years are more likely to be victims of trauma.

11. _____ It is important for you to treat adolescents as if they were adults.

12. _____ Birth defects are the leading cause of death among toddlers.

13. _____ Infants are mouth breathers and cannot breathe easily from their noses.

14. _____ Children can compensate well for breathing problems for long periods of time by using their accessory muscles and by breathing faster.

Mark the following statements regarding fever, dehydration, and shock in children T for true or F for false.

15. _____ Febrile children are usually crying, flushed, or warm to the touch.

16. _____ A fever is a sign of an underlying problem, usually an infectious one.

17. _____ A sign of developing shock is an increase in the number of wet diapers.

18. _____ The most dangerous fevers in children are those caused by heat-related emergencies.

19. _____ Dehydration can cause shock in infants and children.

20. _____ Dehydration is not usually associated with abdominal pain.

21. _____ A late indicator of shock is a low systolic blood pressure.

22. Child abuse victims are usually:

A. ethnic minorities.

B. 5 to 10 years of age.

C. abused repeatedly over time.

D. from poor, single-parent families.

23. A 2-year-old child has multiple bruises about the body and an apparent fracture of the right femur. The child is pale, withdrawn, and appears genuinely frightened of you. Because you suspect child abuse, you should:

A. take the child into protective custody.

B. ask the parents why they have been beating the child.

C. call the police immediately and have the parents arrested.

D. tell the parents that the child must be taken to the hospital for treatment and further tests.

24. The pattern of injuries seen in children can differ from that in adults. Which of the following statements about patterns of injuries is **FALSE?**

A. Children cannot tolerate as much blood loss as an adult without going into shock.

B. A child's neck muscles are stronger and are able to protect the head from sudden, violent stress.

C. Even though the pattern of injury in children may differ from that of an adult, the same care is provided.

D. A child can have serious injuries due to blunt trauma of the chest, abdomen, and pelvis without fractures.

25. Which of the following statements about SIDS is true?

A. SIDS is an inherited disorder.

B. SIDS is extremely rare in the United States today.

C. Children with SIDS are usually victims of child abuse.

D. The parents of SIDS infants need a great deal of comforting.

26. Pediatric patients are divided into developmental stages. Each stage has typical behavior patterns and specific medical problems. These groupings are:

A. less than 1 month, 1 to 24 months, and 2 to 18 years.

B. less than 1 month, 1 to 12 months, 1 to 5 years, and 5 to 18 years.

C. birth to 1 year, 1 to 5 years, 5 to 12 years, and 12 to 18 years.

D. birth to 1 year, 1 to 3 years, 3 to 6 years, 6 to 12 years, and 12 to 18 years.

27. An 11-year-old girl who has been sexually molested is sitting in a chair, sobbing hysterically. Her clothes are torn; there are bruises on her face, and blood on her dress. She also appears to have a broken wrist. She is surrounded by a crowd of anxious, angry friends and relatives. Two police officers are on the scene. As you await the arrival of a female EMT-B, you should:

A. encourage her friends to leave.

B. treat the bruises and splint the wrist.

C. conduct a thorough vaginal examination.

D. allow the police to continue questioning the girl.

28. List four common infectious childhood diseases.

29. Describe "shaken baby syndrome" and the injuries it causes.

30. List six steps you should take to handle possible child abuse.

31. Name the only two conditions under which you should mechanically attempt to dislodge a foreign body from the airway.

32. List five common signs of shock in an infant or child.

33. List five problems you may see when treating a child with a tracheostomy tube.

Ambulance Operations

Mark the following statements about ambulance supplies and equipment T for true or F for false.

1. _____ Equipment and supplies should be placed in the unit according to their relative importance and frequency of use.

2. _____ The jump kit contains an oxygen bottle, defibrillator, and a portable suctioning unit.

3. _____ When attached to an oxygen supply, with the oxygen reservoir in place, a BVM device can supply almost 50% oxygen to the patient.

4. _____ The nonrebreathing valve on a mask must permit inhalation of oxygen during both artificial ventilation and spontaneous respirations.

5. _____ Oxygen masks should be transparent to help you detect respiratory abnormalities or vomiting.

6. _____ The ambulance should have both portable and "on-board" installed suctioning units.

7. _____ A CPR board is a pocket-sized reminder that the EMT-B carries to help recall CPR procedures.

8. _____ Having the ability to exchange equipment between units or between your unit and the emergency department decreases the time that you and your unit must stay at the hospital.

9. _____ Epinephrine in premeasured doses should be carried on your unit.

Mark the following statements about operating the ambulance T for true or F for false.

10. _____ In most instances, if the patient is properly assessed and stabilized at the scene, speed during transport is unnecessary, undesirable, and dangerous.

11. _____ The en route or response phase of the emergency call is the least dangerous for the EMT-B.

12. _____ Disc booster brakes improve braking efficiency, but they increase sway.

13. _____ The first rule in safe driving of an emergency vehicle is that speed saves lives.

14. _____ At night, use only low headlight beams for maximum visibility without reflection.

15. _____ When the siren is on, you may speed up and assume that you have the right-of-way.

16. _____ Use the "4-second rule" to help you maintain a safe following distance.

17. _____ The ambulance should usually be parked 100' past the scene on the same side of the road.

18. Which of the following defines hydroplaning?

A. The measure of the grip of a tire

B. The area of contact between a tire and the road surface

C. Driving on tires lifted from the road surface by a sheet of water

D. Transfer of center of mass to various locations in a moving ambulance

19. An ambulance must be staffed with at least:

A. one EMT-B on board.

B. one EMT-B in the patient compartment when a patient is being transported.

C. two EMT-Bs on board.

D. two EMT-Bs in the patient compartment when a seriously ill patient is being transported.

20. Which of the following does **NOT** need to be included in the daily vehicle safety check?

A. Fuel status

B. Battery(ies)

C. Brake liners

D. All interior and exterior lights

21. Which of the following is one of the most significant developments in ambulance design over the past 20 years?

A. Improved warning systems

B. Exterior vehicle marking systems

C. Computerized oxygen delivery systems

D. Increased dimensions of the patient compartment

22. Patients often report that the most frightening part of becoming suddenly ill or injured is:

A. the illness or injury.

B. not having a current will.

C. a lack of health insurance.

D. the ambulance ride to the hospital.

23. You should never approach a helicopter from the:

A. rear.

B. front.

C. pilot's side.

D. passenger's side.

24. If a helicopter must land on a grade, you must approach the aircraft only from the:

A. rear.

B. front.

C. uphill side.

D. downhill side.

25. Which of the following supplies is **NOT** carried in the jump kit?

A. Oral glucose

B. Defibrillator

C. Trauma shears

D. Blood pressure cuff

26. Suctioning units must be powerful enough to provide an airflow of how many liters per minute?

A. 30

B. 50

C. 90

D. 100

27. During a nighttime helicopter landing, EMTs on the ground can best help the pilot by:

A. placing flares around the landing site.

B. waving white flags in a circle around the landing site.

C. directing light beams toward the ground at the landing site.

D. shining spotlights into the air when the helicopter is approaching.

28. The emergency medical supplies should be checked at least:

A. every 8 hours.

B. daily.

C. weekly.

D. monthly.

29. Which of the following information should the dispatcher gather and record for every emergency request?

      1. Nature of the call

      2. The name, present location, and call-back telephone number of the person calling the location of the patient

      3. The location of the patient

      4. The number of patients and some idea of the severity of their condition

      5. Other problems or information concerning hazards or weather conditions

  A. 1, 2, 3

  B. 1, 3, 5

  C. 2, 3, 4

  D. 1, 2, 3, 4, 5

30. Describe a jump kit.

31. List the equipment and supplies that should be at the head of the primary litter.

32. List the equipment and supplies that should be at the side of the litter.

33. Name and briefly describe two basic types of air ambulances.

34. List three basic universal principles you must follow to legally and appropriately use the warning lights and sirens.

35. State the purpose of deceleration or stopping straps and how they are used.

36. List three patient transfer devices each ambulance should carry.

Scene Techniques

For each of the terms in the left column, select the most appropriate description in the right column. Each description may be used once, more than once, or not at all.

1. _____ multiple-casualty situation (MCS)

    A. a measure of the risk that anyone is subjected to by contact with a certain hazardous material

2. _____ extrication

    B. assists emergency personnel in identifying and handling hazardous materials transport incidents

3. _____ incident management systems

    C. an event that places such a demand upon available equipment or personnel resources that the system is stretched to its limit

4. _____ toxicity level

    D. a measure of the amount of protective equipment that someone must have to avoid injury during contact with a hazardous material

5. _____ triage

    E. a technique of establishing treatment and transport priorities in situations with more than one patient

6. _____ Chemical Transportation Emergency Center (CHEMTREC)

    F. organizational systems to help control, direct, and coordinate emergency responders and resources

7. _____ protection level

    G. removal from entrapment or a dangerous situation or position

For each of the injuries in the left column, select the appropriate triage priority level the injury would be assigned. Each level may be used once, more than once, or not at all.

8. _____ partial-thickness burns on the lower back   A. highest priority (red)

9. _____ abdominal evisceration   B. second priority (yellow)

10. _____ pulseless and not breathing   C. lowest priority (green)

11. _____ swollen ankle   D. lowest priority (black)

12. _____ airway and breathing difficulties

13. _____ uncontrolled bleeding from the thigh

14. _____ decreased level of consciousness

15. _____ shock (hypoperfusion)

16. _____ minor soft tissue injuries

17. _____ decapitation

18. _____ back injuries with spinal cord damage

Mark the following statements about gaining access T for true or F for false.

19. _____ The first step in simple extrication access is to try to get to the patient as quickly as possible using tools or other forcible entry methods.

20. _____ If you will be involved with extrication, you should wear leather gloves over your disposable gloves.

21. _____ When gaining access to an unconscious patient, it is important to talk to him or her and describe what you are doing as you do it.

22. _____ The exact way you gain access or reach a patient will depend on the type of incident.

23. _____ When removing a patient from a vehicle, quick, smooth movements reduce the risk of further injury.

Mark the following statements about hazardous materials T for true or F for false.

24. _____ When you are responding to a hazardous materials incident, you must take time to accurately assess the scene.

25. _____ Moving patients from the contaminated area is your main responsibility in a hazardous materials situation.

26. _____ When you are the first to arrive at the scene of a hazardous materials incident, you should try to read labels and identification numbers from a distance, using binoculars if necessary.

27. _____ Emergency treatment of hazardous materials exposure is primarily aimed at supportive care.

28. _____ In the majority of hazardous materials situations in which a patient has actually been exposed, you should expect quite a long period of time to pass before a decontaminated patient is brought to you for care.

29. _____ Toxicity level 1 is more dangerous than level 4.

30. _____ Protective clothing level A is for greater hazards than level D.

31. _____ If you arrive first at a hazardous materials incident, your job is to fill in for the HazMat team until they arrive.

Mark the following statements about triage T for true or F for false.

32. _____ The triage officer should not become involved in patient care.

33. _____ The lowest priority is given to patients with very minor injuries, those who are not injured, and those unlikely to survive catastrophic injuries.

34. _____ Patients with major or multiple bone or joint injuries should be assigned to the second priority triage category.

35. _____ Patients with severe burns should be assigned to the black triage category.

36. _____ Changing a patient's assigned category is the responsibility of the communications operator.

37. Which of the following steps at the scene sequences is correct and offers the best protection for you and your patient?

A. Size-up, gain access, secure the scene, give care

B. Size-up, secure the scene, gain access, give care

C. Give care, size-up, gain access, secure the scene

D Secure the scene, size-up, gain access, give care

38. It is critical that one person be in charge of the overall rescue operation. Which of the following qualifications is **NOT** necessary for this position?

A. The person must be medically trained.

B. The person must be experienced in extrication.

C. The person must be qualified to judge the priorities of patient care.

D. The person must be a physician trained in emergency medical care.

39. The best way to gain access to a patient trapped in a motor vehicle is to first:

A. try all the doors.

B. break a side window.

C. cut the door lock away.

D. remove the windshield.

40. Which of the following statements about incident management systems is **FALSE?**

A. It provides an orderly means of communication at an emergency scene.

B. It clarifies assignments and the use of personnel and equipment resources.

C. It makes interactions between all the different agencies at the scene easier and simpler.

D. It establishes treatment and transport priorities in situations with more than one patient.

41. Which of the following sources of information may help you identify a hazardous material?

    1. Container labels

    2. Vehicle placards

    3. Shipping papers

    4. Fumes and odors

A. 1, 2, 3

B. 1, 3, 4

C. 2, 3, 4

D. 1, 2, 3, 4

42. List five questions you should ask yourself as you size up a situation.

43. What is the cardinal rule of triage?

44. Name four protection levels and the type of protective gear each requires.

BLS Review

For each of the terms in the left column, select the most appropriate definition in the right column. Each definition may be used once, more than once, or not at all.

1. _____ artificial ventilation

A. establishing artificial ventilation and circulation in a patient who is not breathing and has no pulse

2. _____ abdominal-thrust maneuver

B. essential noninvasive emergency lifesaving care used for patients in respiratory or cardiac arrest

3. _____ basic life support (BLS)

C. lacking oxygen

4. _____ advanced life support (ALS)

D. advanced lifesaving procedures, such as cardiac monitoring, starting IV fluids, and using advanced airway adjuncts

5. _____ artificial circulation

E. a method of dislodging food or other material from the throat of a choking victim

6. _____ cardiopulmonary resuscitation (CPR)

F. provides blood circulation to the body by external chest compressions

7. _____ ischemia

G. opening the airway and restoring breathing by mouth-to-mask ventilation and by the use of mechanical devices

8. _____ Heimlich maneuver

Mark the following statements about BLS care T for true or F for false.

9. _____ During the initial assessment, you need to quickly evaluate the patient's airway, breathing, circulation, and level of consciousness.

10. _____ If you are alone with an adult patient in need of BLS, you should begin CPR first and then call for additional help.

11. _____ All unconscious patients need all elements of BLS.

12. _____ A patient who is not fully conscious often needs some degree of BLS.

13. _____ BLS measures should not be performed on a patient with only a head or spinal injury.

14. _____ Level of consciousness is a good guide to the extent of BLS the patient needs.

15. _____ You should not start CPR if the patient has obvious signs of irreversible death.

Mark the following statements about one-rescuer adult CPR T for true or F for false.

16. _____ After you apply pressure to depress the sternum, you must follow with an equal period of relaxation.

17. _____ The ratio of compressions to relaxation should be 2:1.

18. _____ A lacerated liver is one complication that can develop as a result of external chest compressions.

19. _____ When performed correctly, external chest compressions provide 90% of the blood normally pumped by the heart.

20. _____ The ratio of compressions to ventilations is 15:2.

Mark the following statements about opening the airway and artificial ventilation in infants and children T for true or F for false.

21. _____ In children 1 to 8 years of age, the chin-lift maneuver alone is preferred for opening the airway.

22. _____ For infants, the preferred technique of artificial ventilation is mouth-to-nose-and-mouth ventilation with a mask or other barrier device.

23. _____ You need to use less ventilatory pressure to inflate a child's lungs because the airway is smaller than that of an adult.

24. Which of the following statements about gastric distention is **FALSE?**

A. It commonly occurs in children.

B. It is most likely to occur if you blow too hard during ventilation.

C. It is most likely to occur if you give several rapid breaths in a row.

D. It can be best relieved by pressing on the abdomen while the patient is supine.

25. The most important clinical sign indicating that the patient has started breathing again is the:

A. return of the pulse.

B. movement of the chest.

C. movement of the abdomen.

D. presence of air moving at the patient's mouth and nose.

26. When you are positioning a patient for CPR, he or she should be:

A. log rolled facedown.

B. placed in the recovery position.

C. lying supine on a soft surface, such as a bed.

D. lying supine on a firm surface, such as a long spine board.

27. Which of the following statements about BLS is **FALSE?**

A. It is the same as advanced life support.

B. It can be given by alert and well-trained bystanders.

C. A barrier device should be used to perform rescue breathing.

D. BLS measures are only as effective as the person giving them.

28. List two signs of clinical (or reversible) death.

29. List four signs of biological (or irreversible) death.

30. When resuscitation is started in the field, you must continue until one of the STOP events occurs. STOP stands for:

31. List three steps to perform the jaw-thrust maneuver in an adult.

32. Name four situations where mouth-to-nose ventilation is recommended.

33. The technique for chest compressions needs to be altered in infants and children due to anatomic differences. List four anatomic differences.

34. List four steps to perform the abdominal-thrust maneuver.

35. On the accompanying diagram, shade the area of the sternum where pressure is applied during external chest compression.

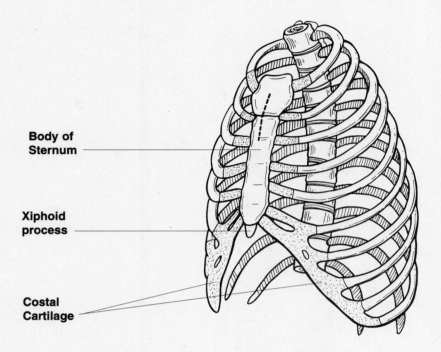

Body of
Sternum

Xiphoid
process

Costal
Cartilage

Infection Control

For each of the terms in the left column, select the most appropriate description in the right column. Each description may be used once, more than once, or not at all.

1. _____ infection

    A. an infection control concept and practice that assumes all body fluids as being potentially infectious

2. _____ designated officer

    B. any disease that can be spread from person to person

3. _____ communicable disease

    C. spread of a communicable disease from one person to another

4. _____ exposure control plan

    D. a comprehensive plan that helps employees reduce their risk of exposure to or acquisition of communicable diseases

5. _____ indirect contact

    E. the individual in the department charged with the responsibility of managing exposures and infection control issues

6. _____ Body Substance Isolation (BSI)

    F. transmission of disease from one person to another by contact with a contaminated object

7. _____ pathogen

    G. the growth of an organism in a susceptible host with or without signs or symptoms of illness

8. _____ universal precautions

    H. the strength or ability of a pathogen to produce disease

9. _____ virulence

    I. a concept for infection control that considers blood and certain body fluids to pose a risk for transmission of blood-borne diseases

10. _____ host

    J. the organism or person in which an infectious agent resides

    K. a microorganism that is capable of causing disease in a susceptible host

For each of the body fluids listed in the left column, select the most appropriate risk factor of PR (Primary Risk), SR (Secondary Risk), or NR (No Risk) in the right column. Each risk factor may be used once, more than once, or not at all. (Note: the category No Risk considers the fluid no risk unless it contains visible blood.)

11. _____ sweat

A. PR (Primary Risk)

12. _____ semen

B. SR (Secondary Risk)

13. _____ saliva

C. NR (No Risk)

14. _____ amniotic fluid

15. _____ blood

16. _____ sputum

17. _____ vaginal secretions

18. _____ vomitus

19. _____ cerebrospinal fluid

20. _____ urine

Mark the following statements about disease transmission T for true or F for false.

21. _____ A communicable disease can be caused by viruses, bacteria, fungi, or parasites.

22. _____ Direct contact occurs when the disease is spread from one person to another by contact with a contaminated object.

23. _____ Hepatitis B and C share the same modes of transmission—contact with blood and sexual contact.

24. _____ You should wear a HEPA respirator if you know or suspect a patient has TB.

25. _____ The single most important measure for personal protection outside of wearing PPE is handwashing.

Mark the following statements about HIV infection T for true or F for false.

26. _____ The HIV virus attacks and destroys certain white blood cells called T4 lymphocytes.

27. _____ The HIV virus is easily killed by drying and by most commonly used disinfectants.

28. _____ HIV is more infectious than the hepatitis virus.

29. _____ There is no vaccine for protection from HIV infection.

30. _____ HIV can be transmitted by swimming pools and hot tubs.

31. Which of the following is considered personal protective equipment (PPE)?

    1. Vinyl and/or latex gloves

    2. Protective eye wear

    3. Cover gowns

    4. Respiratory assist devices

  A. 1, 2

  B. 1, 4

  C. 1, 3, 4

  D. 1, 2, 3, 4

32. Which of the following statements about hepatitis B and C is **FALSE?**

  A. They are caused by two different viruses.

  B. There is a vaccine to protect you from acquiring hepatitis C.

  C. Both hepatitis B and C can lead to long-term liver disease and/or liver cancer.

  D. With hepatitis C, 75% of persons infected do not know that they are infected.

33. List nine areas an exposure control plan should address.

34. List three ways to protect yourself against TB.

35. List five diseases that have been identified as posing an occupational risk for health care providers.

36. Explain what the Ryan White Law is.

37. List six steps you should take after exposure to a patient with HIV infection, or blood or body fluid exposure to a patient with unknown HIV status.

Fundamentals of Extrication

Mark the following statements about scene size-up and the hazard survey T for true or F for false.

1. _____ As extrication proceeds, the size-up and plan should be followed exactly, with no changes.

2. _____ Scene size-up is the responsibility of every rescuer working at an incident.

3. _____ The scene size-up should be completed in 8 to 10 minutes.

4. _____ During a hazard survey, two rescuers should circle the vehicles, in opposite directions, from a distance of 25' to 50'.

5. _____ The safety zone is a 25' to 50' area around the vehicles that is marked with barrier tape or rope.

6. _____ Your unit and other emergency vehicles should remain inside the safety zone.

Mark the following statements about stabilizing a passenger vehicle T for true or F for false.

7. _____ The danger zone for a vehicle that is facing downhill on a slope is the slope below the vehicle.

8. _____ Your hazard survey of a vehicle on a slope should include estimating the center of gravity, assessing the angle of incline, and anticipating the potential direction of movement.

9. _____ If you think a vehicle may roll over the wheel chocks, attach a cable to the bumper to anchor the vehicle.

10. _____ You should make attachments to upright vehicles at their high points.

11. _____ Knowing the estimated center of gravity of a vehicle is critical for proper rigging.

12. _____ Rigging to support the estimated center of gravity increases the potential of vehicle rotation if the vehicle begins to slide or roll.

13. _____ Stabilization of a vehicle on its side is often directed toward widening the base of support.

Mark the following statements about extrication techniques T for true or F for false.

14. _____ Tow truck winches and apparatus winches should be used for expanding hinged passenger vehicle door openings.

15. _____ Grade B rigging chains are used for come-along operations.

16. _____ A cable come-along with rigging chains and cribbing can move vehicle doors in a controlled manner.

17. _____ A hydraulic ram can be used to expand the opening area of a hinged door for both an upright and an inverted vehicle.

18. Which of the following tools is used to break tempered glass?

    1. Spring-loaded center punch

    2. Breaker bar with an extension bar

    3. Halligan bar

    4. Pike pole

A. 1, 2

B. 1, 3

C. 2, 3, 4

D. 1, 2, 3, 4

19. Size-up differs from triage in that size-up involves making decisions about:

A. how to "tag" patients.

B. appropriate extrication procedures.

C. which medical facility is appropriate for each patient.

D. specific treatment requirements for the critically injured.

20. Management of the extrication process, as well as handling the details of patient care, should be determined by:

A. the dispatch center.

B. the fire department.

C. law enforcement personnel.

D. an incident command system or local disaster plan.

21. Which of the following vehicle parts is **NOT** considered an inside electrical hazard?

A. Fuel pump

B. Catalytic converter

C. Two-battery system

D. Radiator cooling fan

22. The most direct method to enter a vehicle is to:

A. remove the doors.

B. break the windows.

C. try to open the doors.

D. raise the steering column and enter through the fire wall.

23. Which of the following is **NOT** a factor when selecting personal protective equipment (PPE)?

A. Trauma from the extrication process

B. Protection from the weather

C. Protection from downed power lines

D. Protection from possible exposure to bloodborne or airborne pathogens

24. During all phases of rescue and extrication operations, your primary responsibilities as an EMT-B are to:

A. keep bystanders away and protect the scene.

B. locate, access, stabilize, and transport the patient.

C. take charge of the rescue operation and extrication process.

D. provide care to the patient and prevent further injury to the patient, yourself, and others.

25. List, in order, the steps in stabilizing an upright vehicle (resting on all four tires).

A. _____ Open the car doors or gain access.

B. _____ Chock the wheels with wood cribbing both in front of and behind the tires.

C. _____ Assess the vehicle for frame/crossmembers or reinforcement points.

D. _____ Establish the safety zone.

E. _____ Place step or box cribbing between the ground and the vehicle.

F. _____ Put the transmission in Park, turn the ignition off, and set the parking brake.

26. Name two effective barriers used to protect the patient and the interior rescuer while a hinged vehicle door is being opened.

27. List three ways to approach the hinge when removing passenger compartment hinged doors.

28. All rescue operations, including vehicle extrication, should follow the four-phase LAST sequence. LAST stands for:

29. List six hazards you should be looking for as you complete a hazard survey.

30. Define the danger zone.

Answer Key

Chapter 1
Introduction to Emergency Medical Care

1. F	**8.** T	**15.** T	**22.** F
2. G	**9.** F	**16.** T	**23.** D
3. B	**10.** T	**17.** F	**24.** B
4. E	**11.** T	**18.** F	**25.** B
5. C	**12.** F	**19.** T	**26.** A
6. D	**13.** T	**20.** F	
7. A	**14.** F	**21.** T	

27.
1. Provide proof of personal immunization as defined in each state
2. Successfully complete a course that follows the 1994 EMT-Basic National Standard Curriculum
3. Mentally and physically meet the criteria of safe and effective practice of job functions
4. Successfully complete a written certification examination
5. Successfully complete a practical certification examination
6. Comply with other state and local provisions

28.
1. Standing orders
2. Protocols
3. Standard medical operating procedures (SMOPs)

29.
1. Establish and maintain an open airway
2. Provide adequate pulmonary ventilation
3. Perform cardiopulmonary resuscitation (CPR)
4. Perform semiautomated external defibrillation (AED)
5. Control external bleeding
6. Treat signs and symptoms of shock (hypoperfusion)
7. Care for cases of poisoning

30. 1. Dispatchers

   2. EMTs

   3. Hospital personnel

   4. Poison control centers

   5. Physicians

   6. Allied health personnel

Chapter 2
The Well-Being of the EMT-B

1.	4, 1, 5, 3, 2	**8.**	F	**15.**	T	**22.**	B
2.	T	**9.**	T	**16.**	T	**23.**	D
3.	F	**10.**	F	**17.**	T	**24.**	B
4.	T	**11.**	T	**18.**	F	**25.**	D
5.	F	**12.**	F	**19.**	T	**26.**	B
6.	T	**13.**	T	**20.**	F	**27.**	D
7.	T	**14.**	F	**21.**	T		

28. It is a confidential group discussion of a highly traumatic incident that usually occurs within 24 to 72 hours of the incident. Its purpose is to relieve personal and group anxieties and stress about the incident.

29. burnout

30. It is an infection control concept and practice designed to approach all body fluids as being potentially infectious.

31. 1. Smoke

   2. Oxygen deficiency

   3. High ambient temperatures

   4. Toxic gases

   5. Building collapse

32. 1. Irritability to co-workers, family, and friends

   2. Inability to concentrate

   3. Difficulty sleeping and nightmares

4. Anxiety

5. Indecisiveness

6. Guilt

7. Loss of appetite

8. Loss of interest in sexual activities

9. Isolation

10. Loss of interest in work

11. Increased use of alcohol

33. 1. Tetanus-diphtheria boosters

2. Measles vaccine

3. Rubella (German measles) vaccine

4. Mumps vaccine

5. Influenza vaccine

6. Hepatitis B vaccine

Chapter 3
Medicolegal and Ethical Issues

1. F	**7.** T	**13.** F	**19.** B
2. D	**8.** F	**14.** T	**20.** C
3. A	**9.** T	**15.** T	**21.** B
4. E	**10.** T	**16.** F	**22.** A
5. C	**11.** T	**17.** D	**23.** C
6. B	**12.** F	**18.** B	

24. If the minor is emancipated, married, or pregnant

25. You must continue to provide all necessary medical treatment until the patient is transferred to another medical professional of an equal or higher level of skill or another medical facility.

26. 1. Obtain the refusing party's signature on an official release form that acknowledges refusal

2. Obtain a signature from a witness to the refusal

3. Keep the refusal with the run report and the medical incident report

4. Write a note about the refusal on the medical incident report and the run report

5. Keep a departmental copy of the record for future reference

27. If there is no written documentation of the DNR order and doubt exists in your mind, you should begin resuscitation. It is better to give treatment than to fail to give treatment.

28. This type of release allows the EMT-B to share information with other health care providers so that they may continue the patient's care. It does not require a written form.

29. 1. In a court of law, if it was not documented, it wasn't done.

2. An incomplete or disorderly record is evidence of incomplete or inexpert medical care.

30. 1. Inform medical control immediately, identifying the patient as a potential organ donor

2. Treat the patient in the same way you would any other patient who needs treatment

3. Take any step necessary to preserve life

Chapter 4
The Human Body

1. F	**14.** A	**27.** C	**40.** T
2. E	**15.** A	**28.** E	**41.** F
3. A	**16.** A	**29.** B	**42.** T
4. C	**17.** B	**30.** F	**43.** F
5. J	**18.** B	**31.** D	**44.** T
6. B	**19.** A	**32.** T	**45.** T
7. D	**20.** A	**33.** F	**46.** C
8. H	**21.** C	**34.** T	**47.** C
9. B	**22.** B	**35.** F	**48.** C
10. B	**23.** C	**36.** T	**49.** A
11. A	**24.** A	**37.** F	**50.** D
12. B	**25.** C	**38.** T	
13. B	**26.** A	**39.** F	

51.
1. Gives the body shape
2. Protects vital internal organs
3. Provides for body movement

52.
1. Cervical (neck), 7
2. Thoracic (upper back), 12
3. Lumbar (lower back), 5
4. Sacral (back wall of the pelvis), 5
5. Coccyx (tailbone), 4

53.
1. Rate
2. Rhythm
3. Quality
4. Depth (tidal volume)

54.
1. Oxygen-rich air enters the alveoli during each inhalation
2. Oxygen-poor blood in the capillaries passes into the alveoli
3. Oxygen enters the capillaries as carbon dioxide enters the alveoli

55.

Component	Function
A. Plasma	Carries blood cells, nutrients; transports waste products
B. Platelet	Permits formation of clots
C. Red blood cell	Provides color, carries oxygen
D. White blood cell	Helps fight infection

56. Blood enters an organ or tissue through the arteries, delivering essential nutrients and oxygen, and leaves through the veins, removing waste products.

57. It is the pressure exerted against the walls of the artery when the left ventricle contracts.

58. It is the remaining pressure exerted against the walls of the artery when the left ventricle is at rest.

59.
1. Central
2. Peripheral

60. 1. Brain

    2. Spinal cord

61. 1. Epidermis

    2. Dermis

    3. Subcutaneous

62. 1. Secretes chemicals

    2. Regulates body activities and functions

63.
A.	Right	G.	Proximal
B.	Superior	H.	Distal
C.	Inferior	I.	Medial
D.	Lateral	J.	Posterior
E.	Midline	K.	Anterior
F.	Left		

64.
A.	Parietal region	F.	Mandible
B.	Temporal region	G.	Frontal region
C.	Orbit	H.	Nasal bone
D.	Zygoma		
E.	Maxilla		

65. A. Occiput

    B. Mastoid process

    C. Temporomandibular joint

    D. Cervical vertebrae

66.
A.	Manubrium	E.	Xiphoid process
B.	Angle of Louis	F.	Costal Arch
C.	Sternum	G.	Ribs
D.	Body		

67.
A.	Brachial	E.	Radial
B.	Posterior tibial	F.	Femoral
C.	Carotid	G.	Dorsalis pedis
D.	Ulnar		

174

68. A. Iliac crest
    B. Ilium
    C. Ischium
    D. Ischial tuberosity
    E. Descending aorta
    F. Sacrum
    G. Anterior superior iliac spine

    H. Inguinal ligament
    I. Femoral artery
    J. Pubis
    K. Symphis pubis

69. A. Thigh
    B. Leg
    C. Foot
    D. Acetabulum
    E. Greater trochanter
    F. Femur

    G. Medial femoral condyle
    H. Lateral femoral condyle
    I. Patella
    J. Tibia
    K. Fibula

70. A. Achilles tendon
    B. Medial malleolus
    C. Talus

    D. Metatarsal
    E. Phalanges
    F. Calcaneus

71. A. Sternoclavicular joint
    B. Sternum
    C. Acromioclavicular joint
    D. Clavicle

    E. Scapula
    F. Acromion process
    G. Glenohumeral joint
    H. Humerus

72. A. Lateral humeral condyle
    B. Olecranon process
    C. Ulna

    D. Humerus
    E. Medial humeral condyle

73. A. Long finger
    B. Ring finger
    C. Little finger
    D. Phalanges
    E. Metacarpals

    F. Carpals
    G. Ulna
    H. Index finger
    I. Thumb
    J. Carpometacarpal joint

74.

A. Nasopharynx   F. Epiglottis

B. Oropharynx   G. Trachea

C. Nasal air passage   H. Major bronchi

D. Mouth   I. Lung

E. Tongue   J. Diaphragm

Chapter 5
Vital Signs and Patient History

1. C	**8.** G	**15.** F	**22.** F
2. E	**9.** F	**16.** F	**23.** A
3. A	**10.** T	**17.** T	**24.** D
4. I	**11.** T	**18.** T	**25.** C
5. D	**12.** F	**19.** T	**26.** B
6. H	**13.** T	**20.** T	**27.** C
7. B	**14.** T	**21.** F	

28.
1. Respirations
2. Pulse
3. Perfusion
4. Pupils
5. Blood pressure

29.
1. Flushed (red)
2. Pale (white, ashen, or grayish)
3. Cyanotic (blue-gray)
4. Jaundice (yellow)

30.
1. Brain injury
2. Cardiac tamponade
3. Tension pneumothorax

Chapter 6
Lifting and Moving Patients

1.	B	**9.**	T	**17.**	F	**25.**	D
2.	A	**10.**	F	**18.**	F	**26.**	B
3.	F	**11.**	F	**19.**	F	**27.**	A
4.	C	**12.**	T	**20.**	T	**28.**	B
5.	E	**13.**	T	**21.**	A	**29.**	C
6.	D	**14.**	T	**22.**	D	**30.**	D
7.	T	**15.**	F	**23.**	C	**31.**	C
8.	T	**16.**	T	**24.**	C		

32.

	Condition	Position
A.	Patient in shock	Legs elevated 8" to 12"
B.	Patient with chest pain or difficulty breathing	Seated in a position of comfort
C.	Patient with suspected spinal injury	Immobilized on a long backboard
D.	Unresponsive patient without suspected spinal injury	Recovery position, rolling patient onto (preferably) the left side, without twisting the body

Chapter 7
The Mechanics of Breathing

1.	C	**9.**	T	**17.**	F	**25.**	B
2.	E	**10.**	F	**18.**	T	**26.**	D
3.	D	**11.**	T	**19.**	D	**27.**	B
4.	H	**12.**	T	**20.**	C	**28.**	C
5.	G	**13.**	F	**21.**	D	**29.**	A
6.	A	**14.**	F	**22.**	C	**30.**	B
7.	F	**15.**	F	**23.**	B		
8.	T	**16.**	F	**24.**	B		

31. A. Trachea   G. Alveoli

        B. Bronchus   H. Pulmonary vein

        C. Pulmonary artery   I. Lung

        D. Heart   J. Venule

        E. Bronchiole   K. Capillaries

        F. Arteriole

Chapter 8
Airway and Ventilation

1. D	**8.** T	**15.** F	**22.** D
2. C	**9.** T	**16.** T	**23.** A
3. B	**10.** F	**17.** F	**24.** A
4. E	**11.** T	**18.** T	**25.** B
5. A	**12.** T	**19.** T	**26.** B
6. T	**13.** T	**20.** B	**27.** D
7. T	**14.** F	**21.** D	

28. 1. Head-tilt maneuver

       2. Head-tilt/chin-lift maneuver

       3. Jaw-thrust maneuver

       4. Modified jaw-thrust maneuver

29. 1. Kneel beside the patient

       2. Straighten the patient's legs and move the nearer arm above the head

       3. Place one of your hands behind the back of the patient's head and neck and the other on the distant shoulder

       4. Turn the patient as a unit toward you

       5. Replace the patient's farther arm back at the side

30. 1. Place your ear 1" above the patient's nose and mouth.

       2. Listen for sounds of breathing and feel for air movement.

       3. Watch to see if the patient's chest and abdomen move with each breath.

Chapter 9
Airway Adjuncts and Oxygen Equipment

1. E	**6.** T	**11.** F	**16.** B
2. C	**7.** T	**12.** B	**17.** C
3. A	**8.** T	**13.** B	**18.** C
4. B	**9.** T	**14.** B	
5. D	**10.** F	**15.** A	

19. 1. A quick-connect female fitting that will accept a quick-connect male plug from a pressure hose or ventilator or resuscitator

     2. A flowmeter that will permit the regulated release of gas measured in liters per minute

20. 1. Those who are not breathing on their own

     2. Those who are not breathing well enough to supply adequate oxygen to the lungs

21. 1. Pressure-compensated

     2. Bourdon-gauge

22. 1. D cylinder (or super D)—can be carried from the unit to the patient

     2. M cylinder—remains on board the unit as a main supply tank

23. 1. Select the proper size airway and moisten it with water to make insertion easier.

     2. Open the patient's mouth with one hand.

     3. Hold the airway upside down with your other hand. Insert it into the patient's mouth with the tip facing the roof of the patient's mouth.

     4. Rotate the airway 180° until the flange comes to rest on the patient's lips and/or teeth. In this position, the airway will hold the tongue forward.

24. It includes a series of pins on a yoke that must be matched with the holes on the valve stem of the gas cylinder. The arrangement of the pins and holes varies for different gases according to accepted national standards. Each cylinder of a specific gas has a given pattern and given number of pins. This system prevents an oxygen regulator from being connected to other gas cylinder regulators and flowmeters that are similar to those used with oxygen. Verifying that the pinholes exactly match the corresponding pins on the regulator is an important safety check.

Chapter 10
Advanced Airway Management

1. B		**9.** T		**17.** T		**25.** F	
2. C		**10.** T		**18.** T		**26.** T	
3. A		**11.** F		**19.** F		**27.** D	
4. E		**12.** F		**20.** T		**28.** B	
5. F		**13.** T		**21.** F		**29.** D	
6. D		**14.** F		**22.** T		**30.** C	
7. H		**15.** F		**23.** F		**31.** D	
8. G		**16.** T		**24.** T		**32.** C	

33.
1. Facilitates suctioning
2. Prevents aspiration and gastric distention
3. Provides complete long-term control and protection of the airway

34.
1. Relieves gastric distention
2. Clears the stomach of blood
3. Clears the stomach of poisons
4. Provides a clear channel to give feedings or medications

35.
1. Intubating the right mainstem bronchus
2. Intubating the esophagus
3. Aggravating a spinal injury
4. Taking too long to intubate
5. Vomiting and/or removing the tube
6. Causing soft tissue trauma

Chapter 11
Scene Size-up and Initial Assessment

1.	G	**8.**	T	**15.**	T	**22.**	D
2.	E	**9.**	F	**16.**	F	**23.**	D
3.	A	**10.**	T	**17.**	F	**24.**	D
4.	B	**11.**	T	**18.**	A	**25.**	C
5.	F	**12.**	T	**19.**	D	**26.**	C
6.	C	**13.**	F	**20.**	D		
7.	F	**14.**	F	**21.**	C		

27.   control any external bleeding

28.   1.   How many patients need medical care?

2.   What is the nature of the patient's illness or the mechanism of injury?

3.   Who contacted EMS?

4.   Is the scene a possible crime scene that needs evidence preservation?

5.   Are hazardous materials involved?

29.   1.   Extend the neck with firm pressure applied to the forehead

2.   Move the patient's head back as far as possible and leave your hand in place

3.   Place the tips of the fingers of your other hand under the bony part of the chin

4.   Lift the chin forward, bringing the entire lower jaw with it

5.   Make sure the chin is lifted enough to bring the teeth together, but the mouth should not close

30.   1.   Direct pressure and elevation

2.   Splinting

3.   Air pressure splinting

4.   Arterial pressure points

5.   Pneumatic air pressure devices

6.   Tourniquets

31.   1.   Are the respirations shallow or deep?

2.   Does the patient appear to be choking?

3.   Is the patient cyanotic (blue)?

Chapter 12
Patient Assessment

1.	B	**8.**	T	**15.**	F	**22.**	A
2.	D	**9.**	T	**16.**	T	**23.**	A
3.	F	**10.**	F	**17.**	F	**24.**	B
4.	E	**11.**	F	**18.**	F	**25.**	B
5.	G	**12.**	T	**19.**	T	**26.**	B
6.	A	**13.**	F	**20.**	D		
7.	C	**14.**	T	**21.**	B		

27.
1. Signs/symptoms
2. Allergies
3. Medications
4. Pertinent past history
5. Last oral intake
6. Events leading to injury/illness

28.
1. Onset
2. Provoke
3. Quality
4. Radiation
5. Severity
6. Time

29. It helps you gather more information about the patient by spending more time inspecting, palpating, and auscultating each area of the body.

30.
1. Deformities
2. Contusions (bruises)
3. Abrasions
4. Penetrations
5. Lacerations
6. Tenderness
7. Burns
8. Swelling

31. 1. Ejection from a vehicle

2. Severe damage to the vehicle, resulting in death of other passenger

3. Falls from higher than 20'

4. Rollover in a vehicle

5. High-speed vehicle collision

6. Pedestrian-vehicle collision

7. Motorcycle crash

8. Blunt head injury

9. Penetration injuries of the head, chest, or abdomen

10. Hidden injuries, such as seat belt or air bag injuries

Chapter 13
Communications and Documentation

1. C		**10.** A		**19.** B		**28.** D
2. H		**11.** A		**20.** T		**29.** D
3. B		**12.** A		**21.** T		**30.** C
4. D		**13.** B		**22.** T		**31.** C
5. A		**14.** A		**23.** F		**32.** C
6. E		**15.** A		**24.** T		**33.** B
7. F		**16.** B		**25.** D		
8. A		**17.** B		**26.** C		
9. A		**18.** A		**27.** D		

34. 1. The patient's name (if you know it) and the mechanism of injury or chief complaint

2. A summary of the information given in your radio report

3. Any important history that was not given already

4. Patient response to treatment given en route

5. The vital signs assessed during transport and after the radio report

6. Any other information gathered that was not important enough to report sooner

35. 1. Chief complaint

2. Level of consciousness (AVPU) or mental status

3. Systolic blood pressure for patients older than 3 years

4. Capillary refill for patients younger than 6 years

5. Skin color and temperature

6. Pulse

7. Respiratory rate and effort

36. 1. Continuity of care

2. Legal documentation

3. Education

4. Administrative

5. Research

6. Evaluation and continuous quality improvement

37. 1. Traditional written form with check boxes and a narrative section

2. Computerized version in which information is filled in using an electronic clip-board or similar device

38. 1. To acknowledge the information and estimate your time of arrival

2. To announce your arrival at the scene

3. To announce your departure from the scene and that you are en route to the receiv-ing hospital

4. To announce your arrival at the hospital or other facility

5. To announce you are clear of the incident or hospital and available for another assignment

6. To announce your arrival at the station or other off the air location

39. See your local instructor

Chapter 14
General Pharmacology

1. A	**7.** A	**13.** B	**19.** T
2. A	**8.** A	**14.** D	**20.** F
3. B	**9.** B	**15.** T	**21.** T
4. B	**10.** A	**16.** T	**22.** C
5. A	**11.** C	**17.** F	
6. B	**12.** A	**18.** T	

23. A potentially life-threatening condition can be treated with little risk to the patient.

24.
1. Tablet
2. Capsule
3. Solution
4. Suspension
5. Metered-dose inhaler
6. Injection
7. Cream
8. Ointment
9. Transdermal patch
10. Sublingual spray

25.
1. Intravenous (IV)
2. Intramuscular (IM)
3. Subcutaneous (SQ or SC)

26.
1. Nitroglycerin
2. Epinephrine auto-injector
3. Metered-dose inhaler

27.
1. Nitroglycerin restores the balance between the heart's work load and the blood flow delivering oxygen to the heart muscle.
2. Nitroglycerin may prevent the development of a heart attack.

28. It opens narrowed or constricted airways and helps restore normal breathing.

29. Make sure there are no open flames, lit cigarettes, or sparks in the area when you are administering oxygen, as oxygen makes it easier for objects to burn.

30. Activated charcoal is usually suspended as a concentrated solution that acts as a laxative.

Chapter 15
Respiratory Emergencies

1.	I	**9.**	H	**17.**	F	**25.**	F
2.	F	**10.**	E	**18.**	T	**26.**	T
3.	A	**11.**	B	**19.**	F	**27.**	T
4.	D	**12.**	F	**20.**	T	**28.**	T
5.	C	**13.**	T	**21.**	T	**29.**	C
6.	H	**14.**	F	**22.**	F		
7.	C	**15.**	T	**23.**	T		
8.	F	**16.**	F	**24.**	F		

30. It is the process in which oxygen enters the blood during inhalation and carbon dioxide and waste products are removed during exhalation.

31. epinephrine

32. They relax the smooth muscles in the bronchial tubes, causing them to open up.

33.
  1. Damaged alveoli
  2. Muscle spasm or mucus obstructs the airway
  3. Air fills the pleural space and the lungs cannot expand
  4. Fluid or infection separate the pulmonary vessels from the alveoli

34.
  1. Normal rate
  2. Regular pattern of inhalation and exhalation
  3. Good audible breath sounds on both sides of the chest
  4. Regular rise and fall movement of both sides of the chest
  5. Movement of the abdomen

Chapter 16
Cardiac Emergencies

1.	C	**14.**	H	**27.**	F	**40.**	F
2.	D	**15.**	T	**28.**	T	**41.**	T
3.	A	**16.**	F	**29.**	F	**42.**	T
4.	B	**17.**	T	**30.**	F	**43.**	T
5.	E	**18.**	T	**31.**	T	**44.**	A
6.	A	**19.**	F	**32.**	T	**45.**	B
7.	G	**20.**	F	**33.**	T	**46.**	B
8.	C	**21.**	T	**34.**	F	**47.**	B
9.	F	**22.**	T	**35.**	F	**48.**	D
10.	E	**23.**	F	**36.**	F	**49.**	C
11.	B	**24.**	T	**37.**	T	**50.**	D
12.	D	**25.**	T	**38.**	F		
13.	I	**26.**	T	**39.**	F		

51.
1. Weakness
2. Nausea/vomiting
3. Sweating
4. Crushing/squeezing chest pain
5. Shortness of breath
6. Epigastric pain
7. Anxiety/apprehension/feeling of impending doom
8. Irregular/abnormal heartbeat
9. Pulmonary edema
10. Abnormal blood pressure/pulse

52.
1. Fully automated—operates without action by the EMT-B, except to turn on the power
2. Semiautomated—uses a computer voice synthesizer to advise the EMT-B what steps to take based upon its cardiac rhythm analysis

53. 1. Follow BSI techniques on the way to the scene

2. Arrive on the scene and perform an initial assessment

3. Stop CPR if it is in progress

4. Verify pulselessness and apnea

5. Have your partner resume CPR

6. Attach the AED

7. Turn on the power

8. Begin speaking if the machine has a tape recorder

9. Stop CPR

10. Clear the patient

11. Start analysis of the rhythm

54. A. Superior vena cava (deoxygenated blood from the head and upper body)

B. Pulmonary artery (blood to right lung)

C. Right atrium

D. Inferior vena cava (deoxygenated blood from lower body)

E. Pulmonary artery (blood to left lung)

F. Right ventricle

55. A. Oxygenated blood to head and upper body

B. Pulmonary veins (oxygenated blood from right lung)

C. Aorta

D. Pulmonary veins (oxygenated blood from left lung)

E. Left atrium

F. Left ventricle

G. Oxygenated blood to lower body

56. A. Common carotid   E. Posterior tibial

B. Brachial   F. Aorta

C. Ulnar   G. Common iliac

D. Femoral   H. Radial

57. A. Superior vena cava

B. Inferior vena cava

C. Common iliac

D. Femoral

Chapter 17
Diabetic Emergencies

1. T	**7.** T	**13.** T	**19.** B
2. T	**8.** F	**14.** T	**20.** A
3. F	**9.** T	**15.** T	**21.** D
4. F	**10.** T	**16.** F	**22.** B
5. T	**11.** F	**17.** C	**23.** B
6. T	**12.** T	**18.** C	

24. The blood glucose level can be checked with a special self-monitoring kit. Patients can keep track of how much glucose is currently in their blood by pricking their finger and reading the strip against a standard table.

25. Insulin is a hormone in the pancreas that enables glucose to enter the cells of the body.

26. When a patient has no insulin, he or she may take a daily injection (or more) of insulin.

27. 1. Have you taken your insulin today?

2. Have you missed a meal today?

3. Have you vomited after eating today?

4. Have you done any strenuous exercise today?

28. 1. Check for medical identification such as a bracelet, tag, or card

2. Ask the patient's family or friends

29. 1. Glutose

2. Insta-Glucose

30. A patient who is unable to swallow or is unconscious should not receive oral glucose since aspiration can occur.

Chapter 18
Allergies and Poisoning

1. G	**9.** F	**17.** T	**25.** D
2. C	**10.** T	**18.** F	**26.** B
3. F	**11.** T	**19.** T	**27.** C
4. B	**12.** F	**20.** F	**28.** C
5. D	**13.** T	**21.** F	**29.** D
6. E	**14.** F	**22.** T	**30.** C
7. A	**15.** T	**23.** C	**31.** D
8. T	**16.** F	**24.** C	**32.** D

33. It attracts the poison, binds to it, and prevents the toxin from being absorbed.

34.
1. Insect bites and stings
2. Medications
3. Food
4. Plants

35.
1. Ingestion
2. Inhalation
3. Injection
4. Absorption

36.
1. Drug overdose
2. Insect sting
3. Animal/snake bite

Chapter 19
Environmental Emergencies

1. D	**5.** B	**9.** A	**13.** F
2. E	**6.** C	**10.** C	**14.** G
3. C	**7.** A	**11.** C	**15.** D
4. E	**8.** E	**12.** E	**16.** B

17. H	22. F	27. F	32. C
18. A	23. T	28. T	33. B
19. T	24. T	29. T	34. B
20. F	25. T	30. F	
21. T	26. T	31. C	

35. one

36. Throw, tow, row, and only then go!

37. 1. Stabilize the vital functions
2. Prevent further heat loss

38. 1. Environment
2. Age of the patient
3. Medical condition of the patient
4. Ingestion of drugs or poisons

39. 1. Amount of time exposed
2. Temperature to which the body part was exposed
3. Velocity of the wind during exposure

Chapter 20
Behavioral Emergencies

1. B	8. T	15. T	22. D
2. D	9. F	16. T	23. C
3. A	10. T	17. F	24. D
4. E	11. F	18. F	25. D
5. G	12. T	19. T	
6. F	13. T	20. F	
7. C	14. T	21. T	

26. 1. Sad, tearful demeanor

    2. Thoughts of death

    3. Patient may not feel like doing anything

    4. Patient may not cooperate

    5. Patient may not answer questions

27. 1. Wide mood swings

    2. Agitation

    3. Panic

    4. Bizarre thinking/behavior

28. 1. Sex

    2. Size

    3. Strength

    4. Mental status

29. head injury or stroke

30. the patient's consent to medical treatment

Chapter 21
Obstetrics and Gynecology

1.	D	8.	A	15.	F	22.	T
2.	C	9.	E	16.	T	23.	B
3.	K	10.	G	17.	T	24.	C
4.	B	11.	T	18.	T	25.	D
5.	H	12.	F	19.	F	26.	C
6.	I	13.	F	20.	F	27.	D
7.	J	14.	F	21.	T	28.	C

29. 1. Place both thumbs one finger breadth below an imaginary line drawn between the nipples on the middle third of the sternum. The rest of your fingers should encircle the chest. Press the two thumbs gently against the lower half of the sternum. Use only enough force to compress the sternum $1/2$" to $3/4$".

2. If your hands are too small to encircle the baby's chest, use your middle and ring fingers of one hand to provide chest compressions. Your other hand should support the baby's back.

30. 1. When delivery can be expected within a few minutes

2. When the hospital cannot be reached due to a natural disaster, weather, or traffic conditions

3. When no transport is available

31. 1. Onset of contractions

2. Bloody show

3. Rupture of the amniotic sac

32. 1. Gently massage the lower abdomen

2. Allow the mother to nurse the baby

Chapter 22
Bleeding and Shock

1.	G	**10.**	A	**19.**	T	**28.**	B
2.	C	**11.**	F	**20.**	F	**29.**	C
3.	E	**12.**	D	**21.**	T	**30.**	B
4.	B	**13.**	B	**22.**	F	**31.**	A
5.	D	**14.**	F	**23.**	T	**32.**	B
6.	A	**15.**	T	**24.**	T	**33.**	B
7.	C	**16.**	F	**25.**	T	**34.**	B
8.	C	**17.**	T	**26.**	F	**35.**	D
9.	E	**18.**	F	**27.**	B		

36. 1. Have the patient sit, leaning forward, with the head tilted forward

2. Apply direct pressure by pinching the nostrils together, or place a rolled gauze bandage between the upper lip and the gum

3. Keep the patient calm and quiet

4. Apply ice over the nose

37. 1. Damage to the heart

2. Dilated blood vessels

3. Inadequate blood volume in the circulatory system

38. 1. Direct local pressure

2. Splinting and elevation

3. Air splinting

39. 1. Agitation, anxiety, or an altered level of consciousness

2. Weak, rapid pulse

3. Pale, ashen, cool, and moist skin

4. Pallor, with cyanosis to the lips

5. Profuse sweating

6. Shallow, labored, or irregular breathing/shortness of breath

7. Nausea or vomiting

8. Marked thirst

9. Capillary refill in infants and children of longer than 2 seconds

40.

Body Part	Activity
1. Muscles	Exercise
2. Gastrointestinal tract	Eating

Chapter 23
Soft Tissue Injuries

1.	D	**9.**	F	**17.**	T	**25.**	C
2.	E	**10.**	C	**18.**	F	**26.**	D
3.	D	**11.**	E	**19.**	T	**27.**	D
4.	G	**12.**	T	**20.**	T	**28.**	A
5.	A	**13.**	F	**21.**	T	**29.**	D
6.	B	**14.**	T	**22.**	F		
7.	A	**15.**	T	**23.**	F		
8.	D	**16.**	T	**24.**	T		

30. 1. To control bleeding

2. To protect the wound from further damage

3. To prevent further contamination and infection

31. 1. Superficial burns

2. Partial-thickness burns

3. Full-thickness burns

32. 1. Depth of the burn

2. Extent of the burn

3. The involvement of critical areas

4. Pre-existing medical conditions or the presence of other injuries

5. The age of the patient

33. I Ice

C Compression

E Elevation

S Splinting

34. 1. There may be a large amount of deep tissue injury

2. The patient may go into cardiac arrest from the electric shock

35. 1. Expose the wound

2. Control the bleeding

3. Prevent further contamination

4. Apply a dry, sterile dressing to the wound and immobilize with bandages and splints

5. Keep the patient calm and quiet

6. Treat for shock if signs and symptoms are present

36. A. Germinal layer   F. Epidermis

B. Pigment granules   G. Sebaceous gland

C. Blood vessel   H. Dermis

D. Sweat gland   I. Nerve

E. Hair   J. Hair follicle

37.Adult:

A. 9%

B. 18%

C. 9%

D. 1%

E. 18%

F. Back: 18%

G. 9%

H. 18%

Child:

A. 9%

B. 13.5%

C. Back: 18%

D. 18%

E. 18%

F. 9%

G. 1%

H. 13.5%

Chapter 24
Musculoskeletal Care

1. I

2. G

3. B

4. H

5. F

6. D

7. A

8. E

9. T

10. T

11. F

12. F

13. T

14. T

15. F

16. T

17. F

18. T

19. T

20. F

21. D

22. D

23. B

24. C

25. D

26. C

27. 2, 4, 3, 5, 6, 1

28.
1. Injuries of the upper extremity
2. Injuries close to or involving the knee
3. Injuries of the hip
4. Injuries of the pelvis
5. Partial amputations or avulsions with bone separation

29. It is the reduction in the amount of bone mass, leading to fractures after minimal trauma.

30.
1. Marked deformity
2. Swelling in the area of the joint
3. Pain that becomes worse with any attempt at movement
4. Almost complete loss of normal motion
5. Tenderness on palpation
6. Loss of pulses distal to the injured site

31. 1. Rigid splint

2. Formable splint

3. Traction splint

32. 1. Pain and tenderness   5. Crepitus

2. Guarding   6. False motion

3. Swelling and bruising   7. Loss of distal pulses

4. Exposed fragments

33. 1. Compression of nerves, tissues, and blood vessels

2. Delay in transport of a patient with a life-threatening injury

3. Impaired distal circulation from applying a splint too tightly

4. Aggravation of the bone or joint injury

5. Conversion of a closed fracture to an open fracture

Chapter 25
Injuries to the Head and Spine

1. D	**9.** C	**17.** C	**25.** C
2. G	**10.** H	**18.** T	**26.** B
3. F	**11.** B or C	**19.** F	**27.** D
4. B	**12.** A	**20.** F	**28.** D
5. I	**13.** C	**21.** T	**29.** A
6. D	**14.** B	**22.** F	
7. A	**15.** A	**23.** D	
8. J	**16.** B	**24.** D	

30. It is a position in which the head is gently lifted until the patient's eyes are looking straight ahead and the head and torso are in line.

31. 1. Neck muscle spasm occurs

2. Pain increases

3. Numbness, tingling, or weakness develops

4. The airway or ventilations become compromised

32. 1. Does your neck or back hurt?

2. What happened?

3. Where does it hurt?

4. Can you move your hands and feet?

5. Can you feel me touching your fingers? Your toes?

33. 1. Epidural—occurs outside the dura mater but under the skull

2. Subdural—occurs beneath the dura mater but outside the brain

3. Intracerebral—occurs within the brain tissue itself

34. A. Frontal lobe   F.   Occipital lobe

     B. Skull   G.   Cerebellum

     C. Temporal lobe   H.   Foramen magnum

     D. Brain stem   I.   Spinal cord

     E. Parietal lobe

35. A. Skin   F.   Arachnoid

     B. Fascia   G.   Blood vessel

     C. Muscle   H.   Cerebrospinal fluid

     D. Skull   I.   Pia mater

     E. Dura mater   J.   Brain

36. A. Cervical   D.   Sacral

     B. Thoracic   E.   Coccygeal

     C. Lumbar

Chapter 26
Infants and Children

1. E		**6.** A		**11.** T		**16.** T	
2. B		**7.** F		**12.** F		**17.** F	
3. C		**8.** T		**13.** F		**18.** T	
4. D		**9.** F		**14.** F		**19.** T	
5. F		**10.** T		**15.** T		**20.** F	

21. T   **23.** D   **25.** D   **27.** B

22. C   **24.** B   **26.** D

28.
1. Measles (rubeola)
2. German measles (rubella)
3. Chicken pox
4. Mumps

29. It is a form of abuse in which an infant's body is forcefully shaken. Severe injury and possible brain damage occur, including bleeding within the head and damage to the cervical spine.

30.
1. Do not attempt to diagnose or accuse when you suspect abuse
2. Maintain a professional, calm, caring approach
3. Record the history and examine the child
4. With possible sexual abuse, do not allow the child to wash, urinate, or defecate
5. Provide transport of all children who are possible victims of abuse, even if their injuries appear minor
6. Report your suspicions to the proper authorities at the hospital

31.
1. The airway is completely blocked, and the patient is unconscious or unresponsive
2. The airway is partially obstructed, and the patient is cyanotic after receiving 100% oxygen

32.
1. Rapid heartbeat
2. Delayed capillary refill
3. Pale, cool, clammy skin
4. Weak or absent peripheral pulses
5. Altered level of consciousness

33.
1. The tube is dislodged
2. The tube is obstructed
3. Bleeding around the tracheostomy site
4. Air leakage
5. Redness, suggesting infection

Chapter 27
Ambulance Operations

1. T		**9.** F		**17.** T		**25.** B
2. F		**10.** T		**18.** C		**26.** A
3. F		**11.** F		**19.** B		**27.** C
4. T		**12.** T		**20.** C		**28.** B
5. T		**13.** F		**21.** D		**29.** D
6. T		**14.** T		**22.** D		
7. F		**15.** F		**23.** A		
8. T		**16.** T		**24.** D		

30. It is a lightweight, durable, waterproof portable kit containing items used in the initial care of the patient.

31. 1. Airway care equipment

2. Artificial ventilation

3. Oxygen delivery

32. 1. Items for cardiac care

2. Bleeding control

3. Blood pressure monitoring

33. 1. Fixed-wing—used for interhospital patient transfers over distances greater than 100 miles

2. Rotary wing—transports of less than 100 miles

34. 1. The unit must be engaged in a true emergency response to your best knowledge

2. Both audible and visual warning devices must be used simultaneously

3. The unit must be operated with due regard for the safety of all others using the roadway

35. They are used to secure the patient to the stretcher. They pass over the shoulders and prevent the patient from continuing forward should the ambulance (and stretcher) abruptly slow down or stop.

36. 1. Wheeled ambulance stretcher

  2. Folding litter

  3. Collapsible chair device

Chapter 28
Scene Techniques

1. C		**12.** A		**23.** T		**34.** T	
2. G		**13.** A		**24.** T		**35.** F	
3. F		**14.** A		**25.** F		**36.** F	
4. A		**15.** A		**26.** T		**37.** B	
5. E		**16.** C		**27.** T		**38.** D	
6. B		**17.** D		**28.** T		**39.** A	
7. D		**18.** B		**29.** F		**40.** D	
8. B		**19.** F		**30.** T		**41.** D	
9. A		**20.** T		**31.** F			
10. D		**21.** T		**32.** T			
11. C		**22.** T		**33.** T			

42. 1. Is the patient in a vehicle?

  2. Is the patient in some other structure?

  3. Is the vehicle or structure severely damaged?

  4. In what position is the vehicle?

  5. On what type of surface is the vehicle?

43. To do the greatest good for the greatest number

44.

Protection Level	Type of Protective Gear
A	Encapsulated protective clothing and gloves
B	Nonencapsulated protective clothing, breathing devices that contain their own air supply, gloves, and eye protection
C	Nonpermeable clothing, eye protection, gloves, and face masks that filter all inhaled outside air
D	Structural fire-fighting clothing and gloves

Appendix A
BLS Review

1. G	**8.** E	**15.** T	**22.** T
2. E	**9.** T	**16.** T	**23.** F
3. B	**10.** F	**17.** F	**24.** D
4. D	**11.** F	**18.** T	**25.** D
5. F	**12.** T	**19.** F	**26.** D
6. A	**13.** F	**20.** T	**27.** A
7. C	**14.** T	**21.** T	

28.
1. Absence of the pulse
2. Absence of breathing

29.
1. Rigor mortis—stiffening of the body after death
2. Dependent lividity (livor mortis)—discoloration of the skin due to pooling of blood
3. Putrefaction or decomposition of the body
4. Separation or obvious destruction of major body organs

30.
S   The patient **starts** breathing and has a pulse.

T   The patient is **transferred** to a higher medical authority in accordance with accepted practice.

O   You are **out** of strength or too fatigued to continue.

P   A **physician** present assumes responsibility for the patient.

31.
1. Kneel above the patient's head. Place your index or middle fingers behind the angles of the patient's lower jaw and forcefully move the jaw forward.
2. Tilt the head backward without significantly extending the cervical spine.
3. Use your thumbs to pull the patient's lower jaw down, to allow breathing through the mouth as well as the nose.

32.
1. It is impossible to open the patient's mouth.
2. It is impossible to ventilate a patient through the mouth because of severe facial injuries.
3. It is difficult to achieve a tight seal around the mouth because the patient has no teeth.
4. You prefer the nasal route for some other reason.

33. 1. Position of the heart

2. Small size of the chest

3. Faster heart rate

4. Relative fragility of the surrounding organs

34. 1. Stand behind the patient. Wrap your arms around the patient's waist.

2. Make a fist with one hand and grasp this fist with the other hand. Place the thumb side of the fist against the patient's abdomen, just above the umbilicus and well below the xiphoid process.

3. Press your fist into the patient's abdomen with a quick inward and upward thrust.

4. Repeat the thrusts in sets of five until the object is expelled from the airway, or the patient becomes unconscious.

35.

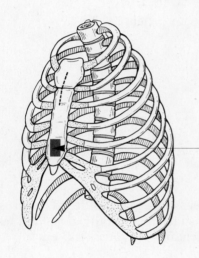

Appendix B
Infection Control

1. G	9. H	17. A	25. T
2. E	10. J	18. C	26. T
3. B	11. C	19. B	27. T
4. D	12. A	20. C	28. F
5. F	13. C	21. T	29. T
6. A	14. B	22. F	30. F
7. K	15. A	23. T	31. D
8. I	16. B	24. T	32. B

33. 1. Determination of exposure

2. Education and training

3. Hepatitis B vaccine program

4. Personal protective equipment (PPE)

5. Cleaning and disinfection practices

6. Tuberculin skin testing/fit testing

7. Postexposure management

8. Compliance monitoring

9. Record keeping

34. 1. Undergo yearly skin testing (called the PPD)

2. Consider infection control issues as you assess patients

3. Wear a HEPA respirator if you know or suspect a patient has TB

35. 1. HIV

2. Syphilis

3. Hepatitis B

4. Hepatitis C

5. Tuberculosis (TB)

36. It requires that the hospital notify your department's designated officer as soon as a patient with an airborne communicable disease is identified. Notification must take place within 48 hours of the time the hospital identifies the patient's disease.

37. 1. Complete an incident report form

2. Notify the designated officer

3. Get counseling before undergoing HIV testing

4. Sign an informed consent form and undergo HIV testing at the time of exposure

5. Retest for HIV at 6 weeks, 12 weeks, and possibly 6 months

6. Get counseling after HIV testing to review the results of each test

Fundamentals of Extrication

1. F	**8.** T	**15.** F	**22.** C
2. T	**9.** F	**16.** T	**23.** C
3. F	**10.** F	**17.** T	**24.** D
4. T	**11.** T	**18.** B	**25.** 3, 2, 5, 1, 6, 4
5. T	**12.** F	**19.** B	
6. F	**13.** T	**20.** D	
7. T	**14.** F	**21.** B	

26.
  1. Short and/or long backboards
  2. Heavy aluminized blanket

27.
  1. Break the hinge attachment point away from the door or car body
  2. Unbolt the hinge
  3. Cut the hinge

28.
  1. Locate the victims at risk or injured
  2. Access the victim, ensuring scene safety
  3. Stabilize the patient to prepare for transport
  4. Transport the patient to the hospital

29.
  1. Traffic
  2. Fire
  3. Electrical hazards
  4. Problems with vehicle stability
  5. Location, number, and condition of patient(s)
  6. Unusual sounds or odors

30. It is an area at the scene that is immediately dangerous to health and life.